Implementing
ISO/IEC 17025:2005

Also available from ASQ Quality Press:

The Quality Calibration Handbook
Jay L. Bucher

The Uncertainty of Measurements: Physical and Chemical Metrology Impact and Analysis
S.K. Kimothi

The Metrology Handbook, Second Edition
Jay L. Bucher, editor

The Certified Quality Technician Handbook, Second Edition
H. Fred Walker, Donald W. Benbow, and Ahmad K. Elshennawy

The Certified Quality Inspector Handbook, Second Edition
H. Fred Walker, Ahmad K. Elshennawy, Bhisham C. Gupta, and Mary McShane Vaughn

The Quality Toolbox, Second Edition
Nancy R. Tague

The Certified Six Sigma Green Belt Handbook
Roderick A. Munro, Matthew J. Maio, Mohamed B. Nawaz, Govindarajan Ramu, and Daniel J. Zrymiak

The Certified Manager of Quality/Organizational Excellence Handbook: Third Edition
Russell T. Westcott, editor

The Certified Six Sigma Black Belt Handbook, Second Edition
T.M. Kubiak and Donald W. Benbow

The ASQ Auditing Handbook, Fourth Edition
J.P. Russell, editor

The Internal Auditing Pocket Guide: Preparing, Performing, Reporting and Follow-up, Second Edition
J.P. Russell

Root Cause Analysis: Simplified Tools and Techniques, Second Edition
Bjørn Andersen and Tom Fagerhaug

To request a complimentary catalog of ASQ Quality Press publications, call 800-248-1946, or visit our website at http://www.asq.org/quality-press.

Implementing
ISO/IEC 17025:2005

A Practical Guide

Bob (Bhavan) Mehta

ASQ Quality Press
Milwaukee, Wisconsin

American Society for Quality, Quality Press, Milwaukee 53203
© 2013 by ASQ
All rights reserved.
Printed in the United States of America
18 17 16 15   5 4 3 2

Library of Congress Cataloging-in-Publication Data

Mehta, Bob, 1961–
    Implementing ISO/IEC 17025:2005 : a practical guide / Bob (Bhavan) Mehta.
    pages cm
    Includes bibliographical references and index.
    ISBN 978-0-87389-854-6 (alk. paper)
    1. Laboratories—Accreditation—Standards. 2. Laboratories—Standards.
I. Title. II. Title: ISO/IEC 17025:2005.
    QC100.A2M44 2013
    001.402′18—dc23

                                                          2013004340

Publisher: William A. Tony
Acquisitions Editor: Matt Meinholz
Project Editor: Paul Daniel O'Mara
Production Administrator: Randall Benson

ASQ Mission: The American Society for Quality advances individual, organizational, and community excellence worldwide through learning, quality improvement, and knowledge exchange.

Attention Bookstores, Wholesalers, Schools, and Corporations: ASQ Quality Press books, video, audio, and software are available at quantity discounts with bulk purchases for business, educational, or instructional use. For information, please contact ASQ Quality Press at 800-248-1946, or write to ASQ Quality Press, P.O. Box 3005, Milwaukee, WI 53201-3005.

To place orders or to request a free copy of the ASQ Quality Press Publications Catalog, visit our website at http://www.asq.org/quality-press.

 Printed on acid-free paper

 Quality Press
600 N. Plankinton Ave.
Milwaukee, WI 53203-2914
E-mail: authors@asq.org

ASQ The Global Voice of Quality™

First, to my late father, who passed away when I was in college in India. He taught me to believe in myself, work hard, and stay determined in everything that I do. I kept these values with me when I came to the United States in 1986. Since then, I never looked back. You are the inspiration for my lifelong passion for learning and for sharing my knowledge with others. You were strict, but you nurtured love and support to make me what I am today.
Thank you, Dad.

To my wife Nina, for her love and support for over two decades. Your support while I wrote this book after working long hours as a consultant was invaluable to me.

To my son Jay, for his love and support, including proofreading the manuscript for this book and sharing ideas as a young quality professional.

And to the American Society for Quality sections around the world and the members of the Orange Empire Section, to which I belong.

Limit of Liability/Disclaimer of Warranty

The author has put forth his best effort in compiling the content of this book; however, no warranty with respect to the material's accuracy or completeness is made. Additionally, no warranty is made in regard to applying the recommendations made in this book to any business structure or environment. The advice and recommendations provided within this book may not be suitable for all business structures or environments. Businesses should consult regulatory, quality, and/or legal professionals prior to deciding on the appropriateness of advice and recommendations made within this book. The author shall not be held liable for loss of profit or other commercial damages resulting from the employment of recommendations made within this book including special, incidental, consequential, or other damages.

Contents

List of Figures and Tables

Preface

The purpose of this book is to demystify the requirements delineated within ISO/IEC 17025:2005 while providing a road map for organizations that wish to receive accreditation for their laboratories. AS9100, ISO 9001, and ISO 13485 are standards that support the development and implementation of effective approaches to quality management and are recognized blueprints for the establishment of a quality management system (QMS) for diverse industries. Although similar to these recognized QMS standards, ISO/IEC 17025 serves a unique purpose: laboratory accreditation. It is not unusual for laboratories to retain dual certification in ISO 9001 and ISO/IEC 17025. However, ISO/IEC 17025 contains requirements specific to the laboratory environment not addressed by ISO 9001. This book highlights the differences between ISO 9001 and ISO/IEC 17025 while providing the practical insight and tools needed for laboratories wishing to achieve or sustain ISO/IEC 17025 accreditation.

ACKNOWLEDGMENTS

I have worked for organizations that design, develop, and manufacture products regulated by the FDA and global regulatory agencies. While I was working in analytical and quality control labs, it became apparent that reliable and properly calibrated equipment was critical to consistently generate accurate data for identity, strength, purity, and efficacy of products. I was inspired to write this book when providing services as a consultant to my pharmaceutical, biotechnology, medical device, active pharmaceutical ingredient, dietary supplement, food, and aerospace clients. I would like to acknowledge Orest Olejnik (Allergan), Gary Swanson (Herbalife), and Lance Harding (Herbalife) for inspiring me to gain the knowledge to create this book. I would also like to acknowledge my direct reports, colleagues, supervisors, professors, students, relatives, and friends for their support, and the staff at ASQ Quality Press and Kinetic Publishing Services.

PART I

Management Requirements

1

Organization

Clause 4.1 of ISO/IEC 17025:2005 identifies the salient requirements for establishing an effective organization. If an organization is seeking accreditation to ISO/IEC 17025 and an approved ISO 9001:2008 quality management system (QMS) has already been certified by a recognized registrar, then the chances are good that an acceptable organizational infrastructure has already been established. The legal entity of the laboratory and its relationship to a parent organization or subsidiaries must be clearly identified. Additionally, the laboratory's management system, policies, procedures, organizational structure, personnel responsibilities and interrelationships, key management personnel, and methods of communication must be defined and developed in the context of complying with ISO/IEC 17025. Furthermore, the primary task of a laboratory is to perform testing and calibration activities in accordance with ISO/IEC 17025. Finally, arguably the most important point for a laboratory is the ability to meet and hopefully exceed the expectations of its customers, including meeting all applicable regulatory and statutory requirements. This initial chapter will examine the requirements and the steps necessary for a laboratory to comply with clause 4.1 of ISO/IEC 17025:2005—Organization.

Summary of ISO/IEC 17025:2005 Requirement 4.1 (Organization)

- An organization is classified as a stand-alone laboratory or the legal entity that is legally responsible for the laboratory.

- The laboratory performing testing and calibration must do so in accordance with ISO/IEC 17025:2005 and applicable regulatory and statutory requirements. Meeting customer requirements is a fundamental expectation.

- When laboratories are part of organizations that perform more than just testing and calibration, responsibilities of key personnel must be clearly defined to prevent any conflict of interest.

- Laboratories must:

  —Retain adequate management and technical personnel with sufficient authority to support the implementation, maintenance, and improvement of the management system; when deviations from the established management system occur, these individuals will pursue corrective action to mitigate deviations, as appropriate

  —Ensure management and personnel are protected from undue influences (internal and external) that may affect the quality of their work

  —Establish policies and procedures to protect the confidentiality of customer data

  —Establish adequate policies and procedures in support of the overall operational integrity of the lab

  —Adequately define the organizational structure

  —Delineate the authority, responsibility, and interrelationships of laboratory personnel

  —Provide adequate supervision of all laboratory personnel

  —Retain technical management responsible for technical operations

—Appoint a quality manager with a direct reporting line to senior management

—When deemed appropriate, identify and appoint deputies for key management personnel

—Ensure all personnel clearly understand the influence that the execution of their day-to-day activities has on the management system

EFFECTIVE TOOLS FOR IMPLEMENTATION AND COMPLIANCE

Clause 4.1 is essentially an overview of what is required of laboratory management to maintain an effective management system. For example, the laboratory must retain adequate and properly trained resources to ensure the management system always complies with ISO/IEC 17025. When deviations from the management system are identified, management is tasked with correcting the deviation in accordance with clause 4.11 of ISO/IEC 17025, discussed in Chapter 11 of this book.

To begin with, the creation of an organizational chart is a fundamental requirement for laboratories considering accreditation. A well-constructed organizational chart clearly delineates the functional structure of the laboratory (see Figure 1.1). The roles of the laboratory's quality manager and technical manager must be clearly depicted on the chart.

The fundamental requirement is to ensure that the roles, responsibilities, and authority established within the laboratory are adequate and in compliance with ISO/IEC 17025. Chapter 17 discusses the importance of having a job description in greater detail; however, it is strongly recommended that job descriptions contain the reporting structure for each job. For example, the calibration technicians report directly to the test and calibration supervisor.

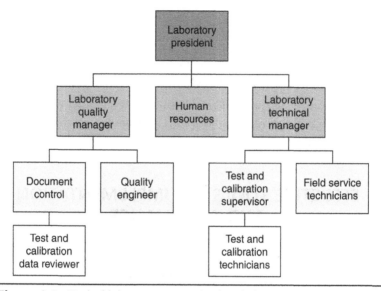

Figure 1.1 Typical laboratory organizational chart.

Additionally, all laboratory employees must be trained to understand the influence their functional duties have on the overall effectiveness of the laboratory's management system. Most organizations accomplish this task through initial employee orientation and training. Regardless of the approach pursued, the training must be documented in accordance with clause 5.2 of ISO/IEC 17025 (see Chapter 17).

It is also important that the laboratory appoint a quality manager and a technical manager and delineate the specific roles and responsibilities for each of these positions. Once again, the job description will play a key role in defining duties and responsibilities.

Finally, laboratories must ensure the confidential nature of customer data. ISO/IEC 17025 requires that laboratories prepare a policy and procedure document that defines the protection of confidentiality process. The procedure should be prescriptive when it comes to defining the security of confidential data.

QUESTIONS TO CONSIDER DURING AN AUDIT

The questions in this section are not intended to be an all-inclusive list to be built into an internal or external audit checklist. However, they are relevant when evaluating the overall effectiveness of a laboratory's organizational structure.

1. Is the laboratory a stand-alone entity or part of a larger organization?

2. Is the laboratory currently accredited to ISO/IEC 17025: 2005?

3. Is the certificate of accreditation current?

4. Does the laboratory have a documented management system that delineates all policies, procedures, and work instructions used during testing and calibration?

5. Has the laboratory created an organizational chart?

6. Has a policy and procedure been established that protects the confidentiality of customer information?

7. Have responsibility and authority levels for all employees been established?

8. Does the laboratory have a designated quality manager?

9. Does the laboratory have a designated technical manager?

CHAPTER REVIEW

There are four fundamental requirements needed to achieve compliance with clause 4.1 of ISO/IEC 17025. For starters, the laboratory must identify roles, responsibilities, and levels of authority for employees. The organizational chart is the perfect tool to accomplish this requirement. Second, job descriptions should be clear and concise in regard to reporting relationships. Third, a policy and procedure document must be written that delineates the laboratory's approach to protecting and securing the confidentiality of a client's data. Finally, the laboratory must appoint a quality manager and a technical manager.

As for maintaining the effectiveness of the management system and employing corrective action and preventive action (CAPA) to correct deviations, this is expected of all accredited laboratories. Without a management system and all of the supporting policies and procedures that ensure the ongoing effectiveness of the management system, meeting customer expectations—a fundamental requirement of ISO/IEC 17025—becomes a daunting challenge.

2

Management System

Any organization operating in a regulated environment must establish a fundamentally sound and effective QMS that complies with regulatory requirements, statutory requirements, and recognized standards such as those authored by the International Organization for Standardization (ISO) and the International Electrotechnical Commission (IEC). AS9100, ISO 9001, and ISO 13485 are standards that have been developed to support the development and implementation of effective approaches to quality management and are recognized blueprints for the establishment of a QMS for many diverse industries. Although similar to these recognized QMS standards, ISO/IEC 17025 serves a unique purpose: laboratory accreditation. One thing the reader should keep in mind is the importance of the link between ISO 9001 and ISO/IEC 17025. Laboratories that are accredited in and operate in accordance with ISO/IEC 17025 are expected to comply with clauses of ISO 9001 as they pertain to the laboratory environment. It is not uncommon for a laboratory such as a metrology lab to possess dual certification/accreditation in ISO 9001 and ISO/IEC 17025. However, some requirements are unique to ISO/IEC 17025, such as the technical competency of laboratory personnel, the use of validated testing methodologies, and ongoing proficiency testing for laboratory personnel. One way to view the differences between these two standards is that

ISO 9001 provides guidance for an effective QMS and ISO/IEC 17025 drives technical competency within a QMS.

The management system will form the foundation for any facility wishing to achieve accreditation in ISO/IEC 17025. As in the case of ISO 9001, the quality manual becomes a core document used to describe the management system. Other requirements in support of complying with ISO/IEC 17025 are (1) written procedures; (2) a concise quality policy statement; (3) management's commitment to develop, implement, and continuously improve the management system; (4) management's communication and reinforcement to the organization of the importance of meeting customer and regulatory requirements; (5) reference(s) to procedures in the quality manual; (6) the definition of the roles and responsibilities of technical management and the organization's quality manager; and (7) ongoing sustainment of the integrity of the management system by quality.

Summary of ISO/IEC 17025:2005 Requirement 4.2 (Management System)

- Laboratories are required to develop and implement a QMS that delineates the organization's policies, systems, programs, and procedures in support of performing testing and calibration activities. The laboratory must establish a clear path of communication that supports the communication and training of QMS content to employees.

- The laboratory is expected to prepare a quality manual that defines fundamental quality policies influencing the QMS, including a robust quality policy and clearly defined objectives. The quality policy and objectives are required inputs into management review.

- The requirements of the quality policy statement are prescriptive and should include:

—A commitment statement to good professional practice (GPP) from management

—A standard of service statement

—The purpose of the QMS

—A requirement that all laboratory personnel familiarize themselves with the quality procedures and policies

—A commitment statement from management to implement continuous improvement activities needed to drive QMS effectiveness

—A commitment statement from management to comply with ISO/IEC 17025:2005

- Laboratories are required to provide evidence that they continuously work toward improving and strengthening the QMS.

- Management must ensure that the entire organization remains aware of the importance of meeting not only customer requirements but also regulatory and national, state, and local statutory requirements.

- The quality manual must include a list of procedures or a pointer to the location of the list of procedures. Additionally, the quality manual must contain an outline of the documentation hierarchy, the role and responsibilities of the quality manager, and the role and responsibilities of the technical manager.

- Laboratory management is responsible for maintaining the integrity of the QMS when changes are planned and implemented.

EFFECTIVE TOOLS FOR IMPLEMENTATION AND COMPLIANCE

The path toward accreditation begins with the basic under-standing that a laboratory must have an established QMS. Two of the main purposes driving the need for an established QMS are (1) the ability to provide accurate and repeatable testing results, supported by data, to the customer and (2) the ability to maintain accurate records to support the quality of the data provided. As with regulatory requirements enforced by the Food and Drug Administration (FDA), the accreditation bodies require documented evidence of compliance (see ISO/IEC 17011:2004).

The fundamental requirement for achieving compliance with clause 4.2 of ISO/IEC 17025 is the establishment of an effective QMS including: (1) policies, (2) procedures, and (3) work instructions. Additionally, a well-written and succinct quality policy manual is a stand-out requirement. One tool that has proven to be effective in support of developing an effective QMS is a requirements matrix that maps an organization's QMS to ISO/IEC 17025 (see Table 2.1).

The quality policy manual will become the cornerstone of the laboratory's management system. As with ISO 9001, very specific laboratory-focused requirements must be incorporated into the quality policy manual—for example, the laboratory's quality objectives and quality policy statement. The laboratory's objectives, once established, should be reviewed during the management review process (detailed in Chapter 15).

Table 2.1   Sample requirements matrix.

Document number	Revision	Document name	ISO/IEC 17025	ISO 9001
QPM0001	AA	Quality Policy Manual	4.2.2	4.2.1(b); 4.2.2
QSP0002	AA	Quality Policy	4.2.2	4.2.1(a); 5.3
QSP0003	AA	Master Document List	4.2.5	4.2.2(b)
QSP0004	AA	Organizational Chart	4.2.6	5.5.1

However, unlike in ISO 9001, the quality policy statement has very specific requirements that senior laboratory management must authorize and enforce. For example, "We provide world-class calibration services to ensure client success" would not be an acceptable quality policy statement. At a minimum, the quality policy must contain:

- Management's commitment to good professional practice and the quality of services (testing and calibration) provided to clients

- Management's statement in regard to the standard(s) of service

- A definition of the purpose of the management system, as it relates to quality

- A specific requirement that all laboratory personnel be familiar with the laboratory's quality documentation policies, implementation policies, and procedures as part of executing their day-to-day activities

- Management's commitment to comply with ISO/IEC 17025:2005

- Management's commitment to continually strive to improve the overall effectiveness of the management system

An example of a good laboratory quality policy statement is the one drafted and employed by Metal Test Incorporated (see Figure 2.1).

Other requirements for the quality policy manual are:

- A list of procedures (it is acceptable to reference another document, such as a master document list, in the quality manual instead of placing the actual compiled list in the manual)

Quality Policy Statement

To ensure accurate and timely analytical, interpretive, and technical metallurgical services and to continuously meet or exceed the stated or implied expectations of our customers through day-to-day interactions.

a) Management commitment to good professional practice and quality of services provided to the customer: Tests are always carried out in accordance with stated standardized methods and customers' requirements. Requests to perform tests that may jeopardize an objective result or have a low validity are rejected.

b) Standards of service include:

- Customer satisfaction

- Accuracy

- Timeliness

Excellence in the workplace is promoted by providing all employees with the knowledge, training, and tools necessary to allow for the completion of accurate and timely work.

c) Purpose of management system related to quality: To manage our business by meeting the needs of our customers.

d) Personnel familiarize themselves with quality documentation and implement the policies and procedures in their work.

e) Management is committed to:

- Complying with ISO 17025, ISO 9001, and NQA-1 standards

- Aerospace standard AC7006 and AC7101/1

- Continually improving the effectiveness of the management system

---

Figure 2.1   Metal Test Incorporated quality policy statement.

- The roles and responsibilities of the laboratory technical manager and the quality manager (the managers' responsibilities with regard to compliance with ISO/IEC 17025:2005 must be included)

Addressing each clause of ISO/IEC 17025 during the development of the quality policy manual is highly recommended. In some cases, such as in the quality policy statement, significant granularity will be required to meet the intent of the standard. However, in regard to requirements such as 4.2.3, 4.2.4, and 4.2.7, a simple compliance statement placed in the quality policy manual is acceptable.

Additional requirements that laboratory management need to address to achieve compliance with this standard are:

- Evidence of commitment to the development and implementation of a management system

- Evidence of continuous improvement activities in pursuit of improving the management system

- Communicating the importance of meeting customer, regulatory, and statutory requirements to laboratory personnel

- Maintaining management system integrity when changes to the management system are planned and implemented

Including processes specific to meeting these requirements in quality system procedures ensures that these requirements will be woven into the fabric of the laboratory's management system. For example, corrective action, preventive action, customer complaints, and management review are tools used to gauge the overall effectiveness of a laboratory's management system. ISO/IEC 17025 requires written procedures to address these tools. Well-written procedures used to measure the overall effectiveness of the management system will meet the requirements delineated in clause 4.2 of the standard.

QUESTIONS TO CONSIDER DURING AN AUDIT

The questions in this section are not intended to be an all-inclusive list to be built into an internal or external audit checklist. However, these questions are relevant when evaluating the overall effectiveness of a laboratory's management system.

1. Is the laboratory's management system adequately documented with written policies, procedures, and work instructions?

2. Does the laboratory have a quality policy manual?

3. Does the laboratory have a documented quality policy statement?

4. Does the quality policy statement contain:

   - Management commitment to good professional practice, quality, and service

   - Management statement of standard of service

   - The purpose of the management system as it relates to quality

   - The requirement that all employees be familiar with the QMS

   - The laboratory's commitment to comply with ISO

5. Has the quality policy statement been included in the quality policy manual?

6. Have the laboratory personnel been trained in the quality policy? Is there documented evidence of the training?

7. Is there evidence that continuous improvement activities are pursued?

8. How does management communicate the importance of meeting customer requirements?

9. Does the quality policy manual contain a list of quality procedures or make reference to the location of the master list of procedures?

10. Have the role and responsibilities of the laboratory's technical manager been defined?

11. Have the role and responsibilities of the laboratory's quality manager been defined?

12. How is the integrity of the management system maintained when changes to the management system are planned and implemented?

CHAPTER REVIEW

The establishment of a compliant management system supported by a well written quality policy manual is a fundamental requirement of ISO/IEC 17025:2005. ISO 9001 and ISO/IEC 17025 have significant similarities; however, there are differences rooted in the technical competencies and requirements specific to a laboratory environment (testing and calibration). One of these differences is the granularity required for the quality policy statement. Since the quality policy statement is often shared with the customer and typically placed on the laboratory's website, much care should go into drafting the quality policy statement. Another requirement specific to the quality policy manual for laboratories is the inclusion of the responsibility statements for the laboratory's technical manager and quality manager. Additional requirements that result in evidence of compliance, management system effectiveness, and continual improvement of the management system are supported by quality system procedures that are written, reviewed, and approved prior to their implementation. Because the ultimate goal is to achieve and sustain accreditation to ISO/IEC 17025, it is very important not to take shortcuts when establishing the management system. Compliance with all aspects of the standard, regardless of the requirement being written or implied, is mandatory.

3

Document Control

It is impossible to place too much emphasis on the importance of the document control function. In a regulated environment, the control of documentation should be treated as a mission-critical process. It is not enough for organizations to just control documents; they must also manage and control all aspects associated with effective document management. For example, ISO/IEC 17025:2005 includes these requirements: (1) the establishment of documents and procedures, (2) the review of documents and procedures, (3) the approval of documents and procedures, (4) the issuance and control of documents and procedures, (5) the change-control process for documents and procedures, and (6) the removal of obsolete documents and procedures. Experienced quality professionals understand the importance of document control and realize that effective document control can be used as a tool to facilitate successful internal and external quality audits. Although some organizations and laboratories continue to support a manual approach to document control, an abundance of software programs are available to automate the document control process. Regardless of the approach pursued—whether manual or automated—this chapter explores the essential requirements needed to comply with ISO/IEC 17025:2005, clause 4.3—Document Control.

Summary of ISO/IEC 17025:2005 Requirement 4.3 (Document Control)

- Laboratories must establish procedures to control all documents, both externally and internally generated.

Note: Documents are policy statements, procedures, specifications, calibration tables, charts, textbooks, posters, notices, memoranda, software, drawings, and plans—regardless of media.

- All documentation issued within the laboratory must be reviewed and approved. The laboratory shall create and maintain a master list of procedures (including procedures for revisions) and ensure a process exists for the removal of obsolete documents from their point of use.

- The procedure used for document control shall ensure:

  —Only authorized copies of procedures are available for use

  —Documents are reviewed and revised, as appropriate

  —Obsolete documents are quickly removed from their point of use

  —Obsolete documents that are retained, regardless of purpose, are adequately identified

- Management system documents must be appropriately identified and controlled through the use of either a date or a revision designation (e.g., Version AA).

- All document changes must be reviewed and approved.

- Where practical, changes to a document must be adequately identified.

- If a practice of red-lining documentation is permitted by the laboratory, the practice must be documented by procedure.

- If a computerized system is used as part of managing the document control process, a procedure describing the computerized approach must be established.

EFFECTIVE TOOLS FOR IMPLEMENTATION AND COMPLIANCE

An abundance of commercial off-the-shelf software is available that can be quickly implemented to solve the document management dilemma. That being said, the most effective tool in support of meeting the document control requirement is a well written procedure. The key elements of document control are:

- The document numbering system

- The use of revision/version control

- Pagination

- Initial document review and approval

- The master document list

- Document changes

- Control of external documents

- Document availability

- Document storage

- Red-line changes

- Document obsolescence

The Document Numbering System

Building some intelligence into the document numbering system is highly recommended. For example, the use of prefixes such as SOP (standard operating procedure), TM (test method), WI (work instruction), FM (form), TP (test procedure), and QIP (quality inspection procedure) should be considered. Since the functional structure and the industries served may differ among laboratories, creating prefixes relevant to the specific laboratory is acceptable. A set standard does not exist, although SOP is for the most part universally understood.

As for the number, it may be a sequence starting with 1001; for example, "SOP-1001 Document Control" would be an acceptable format. It is also acceptable to align high-level documents, such as a document control procedure, with the actual standard. For example, "SOP-4.3 Document Control" would also be considered acceptable.

Some computerized document control systems do not permit much flexibility, so care should be taken when a laboratory is looking to purchase a solution with a plan to migrate an existing document numbering structure.

The Use of Revision/Version Control

The most widely accepted approach to revision or version (the term used depends on the laboratory) control is the use of alphabetical and numerical characters. It is also an acceptable practice to control revisions through the use of a date, although the practice is less common. Some organizations use both a revision number and a date. Another practice to consider is the use of alphabetical revision characters for released documentation and numerical revision characters for developmental or engineering documentation. The following examples of revision control are acceptable:

- SOP-1001, Revision A or SOP-1001, Version A
- SOP-1001, 10/24/12
- SOP-4.3, Revision A (10/24/12)

Pagination

In regard to pagination, documents, especially procedures, must have legible page numbers. This requirement is delineated in clause 4.3.2.3 of ISO/IEC 17025. It is recommended that the page format be simple (e.g., "page 1 of 4").

Initial Document Review and Approval

All documentation requires some level of oversight, review, and approval. For example, inputting a regulation or a standard may be as simple as the person tasked with document control responsibilities logging the receipt date and entry date of this document into the document control system. For SOPs or TMs written by the laboratory, a detailed review and approval is probably warranted. Typically a document change order (DCO) or engineering change request (ECR) would be used to document this review (see Figure 3.1).

The Master Document List

A master document list (MDL) must be compiled. Many organizations choose to list the documents relevant to the QMS in the quality manual; however, all that is required is a pointer to where the list is located. The MDL should contain a reference to the document revision. The MDL is an excellent tool that can be used to quickly find a document. This type of document is extremely important to have available for external audits. The auditor will ask for the MDL because it is a road map for the laboratory's document structure.

Document Changes

All revisions to documents require the same level of scrutiny that new documents do. A detailed review and subsequent approval are core requirements of a document control system. The laboratory also needs to ensure the reviews of document changes are performed by a cross-functional group. For example, if the document being changed is a test procedure, then engineering, quality, and operations will want to review and, if appropriate, provide input on potential changes. In some cases, customer review and approval may also be required. For these reasons, it is important for the laboratory to be vigilant when processing document changes.

Engineering Change			
Part/Drawing no.	Part description	ECR no.	Date
Reason for change			
Description of change			
Originator name	Signature		Date
Disposition			
☐ Rejected Reason for rejection:			
☐ Approved		Due date	
CAT ☐ I—Initial release ☐ II—Must be implemented by due date			
Quality assurance name	Signature		Date
Engineering name	Signature		Date
Laboratory name	Signature		Date
Closeout			
Current rev.	New rev.	Implementation plan:	Date
Originator name	Signature		Date

Figure 3.1   ECR form.

Control of External Documents

The document control system needs to be able to manage external standards, as well. For example, (1) customer drawings and specifications, (2) standards such as ISO/IEC 17025, (3) regulatory and statutory documents such as 21 CFR Part 820, and (4) test methods such as ASTM need to be input and tracked by the document control system. Laboratories must always have the latest version of a document on file. Companies like IHS (http://www.ihs.com) can augment the document control process by ensuring laboratories have the most up-to-date version of a standard.

Document Availability

The most current version of a document must be made available at the point of use. Considering the abundance of available technology, laboratories should consider placing monitors or other remote terminals capable of accessing documentation in real time at multiple locations to facilitate the ease of access. If a manual system is in use, a kiosk can house the most current documentation and ensure availability of the documents at the point of use. Document availability is a requirement in accordance with clause 4.3.2.2.

Document Storage

The established procedure must contain sufficient granularity to describe the document storage process. If an electronic system is used for document storage, then the process employed for scanning documents into the document control system must be described. If the storage method is manual, then the storage location needs to be clearly identified, including levels of access granted to the document storage area. The preservation of these physical documents should also be considered because they need to be protected from damage during routine storage.

Red-Line Changes

Although red-lining documents to make document changes is acceptable under ISO/IEC 17025, it is better to dissuade laboratory personnel from the practice. Far too often, red-line changes are not properly accounted for when a revision to a document is made. This can result in nonconformance with the accreditation body and/or calibration work needing to be repeated.

Document Obsolescence

Obsolete documentation needs to be clearly identified as such and removed from point of use as quickly as possible. If retaining obsolete documentation at the point of use for historic purposes is necessary, then it should be identified as obsolete with a stamp that describes the status of the document (Figure 3.2).

QUESTIONS TO CONSIDER DURING AN AUDIT

The questions in this section are not intended to be an all-inclusive list to be built into an internal or external audit checklist. However, they are relevant when evaluating the overall effectiveness of document control implemented by a laboratory.

1. Does the laboratory have an established procedure for the control of documents?

2. Does the control of documents procedure address internal and external documents?

3. Are documents reviewed and approved prior to their issuance for use within the laboratory?

4. Are procedures and work instructions available at their point of use?

5. What is the laboratory's approach to revising documents?

**Obsolete
Do Not Use
10-21-2012**

Figure 3.2   Document status stamp.

6. Are obsolete documents identified and removed from use?

7. Are obsolete documents retained as permanent records?

8. Are management system procedures uniquely identified?

9. Are document changes reviewed and approved by the same functional groups tasked with reviewing and approving the initial release?

10. Does the document usage procedure allow for red-line changes to documents?

11. Does the organization use a computerized system in support of the control of documents?

CHAPTER REVIEW

Laboratories are required to establish a procedure that delineates their policy and processes for the effective management of documents. Using an electronic approach to document control is acceptable provided that the requirements delineated in clause 4.3 of ISO/IEC 17025 are achieved. It is important to ensure laboratory-scripted documents are reviewed, approved, and released at their point of use. Additionally, the document control system must be capable of handling external documents. Furthermore, a master document list, including the document revision, must be compiled and retained. Finally, obsolete documents need to be identified as such, and when practical, removed quickly from service.

4

Review of Requests, Tenders, and Contracts

This chapter aligns with clause 7 of ISO 9001:2008, Product Realization. Similar to ISO 9001, ISO/IEC 17025:2005 requires laboratories to establish policies and procedures for the review of customer requests, the identification of laboratory resources, and the selection of appropriate test methods or calibration methods to meet customer requirements. Documented contract reviews are also a salient requirement of ISO/IEC 17025. It is not enough for laboratories to simply review customer and contractual requirements. The decision to accept, request a modification of, or reject a customer order must be documented. Should the laboratory plan to subcontract activities in accordance with ISO/IEC 17025:2005, clause 4.5—Subcontracting of Tests and Calibrations (see Chapter 5), then the use of a contractor must be incorporated into the review process and be disclosed to the customer. Furthermore, it is inevitable that contract deviations will occur. In such cases, ISO/IEC 17025 requires laboratories to notify their customers. Finally, although ISO/IEC 17025:2005 recognizes both oral and written contracts, it is always best to have a written contract that clearly defines customer requirements and expectations. This chapter expands on the importance of reviewing requests, tenders, and contracts.

Summary of ISO/IEC 17025:2005 Requirement 4.4 (Review of Requests, Tenders, and Contracts)

- The laboratory must establish a procedure that outlines the review and handling of requests, tenders, and contracts.

- The procedure used for review must describe:

  —Requirements (e.g., procedures specific to testing and calibration)

  —The laboratory's capability to actually perform the testing and/or calibration

  —Whether the testing or calibration methods selected are capable of achieving stated requirements

  Note: Contracts can be written or oral agreements.

- Records of contract reviews and changes to contracts shall be retained by the laboratory.

- Customer notification of contract deviations is required.

- Contract revisions implemented once work has commenced must be reviewed and changes implemented quickly.

EFFECTIVE TOOLS FOR IMPLEMENTATION AND COMPLIANCE

Having an established procedure for contract review is an important requirement for laboratories. The expectation is that the written procedure be prescriptive enough to support an effective contract review process. One tool that can be implemented quickly is a contract review checklist. The following elements should be considered when developing the checklist:

Contract/Purchase Order Identification

- Has the correct business name of the customer been provided?

- Does the delivery address differ from the business address?

- Has the correct contact information been provided?

- Have all of the necessary drawings and specifications been received?

Scope/Definition of Work or Services to Be Provided

- Is the scope of the work to be performed clear and concise?

- Are other proposals incorporated into the agreement?

- Is the customer going to provide equipment and materials to support laboratory work?

- Does the laboratory have the ability to perform the work defined?

- Will any of the work defined in the scope need to be subcontracted to another source?

Payment/Terms

- Have the payment terms been clearly defined in the contract/purchase order?

- Has a review of the customer's Dun & Bradstreet rating been performed?

Schedule

- Does the contract/purchase order contain delivery dates?

- Can the laboratory meet those dates? (If not, notify the customer and present schedule options.)

- Does the contract/purchase order contain penalties for failing to meet delivery dates?

Contract/Purchase Order Changes and Deviations

- Does the customer have a change order process?

- Is there a deviation notification clause in the contract/purchase order?

- If this is a change order, are the changes accurate?

- Will the change order affect cost or delivery?

Contract Claims and Disputes

- Does the contract/purchase order contain a clause for claims and disputes?

- Is there an arbitration clause for the handling of dispute resolution?

Requirements for Indemnity and Insurance

- Does the contract/purchase order contain an indemnity and insurance clause?

- Has the laboratory identified levels of risk it is willing to assume?

- Are responsibilities for the customer and the laboratory clearly defined?

- Is the laboratory's insurance adequate considering the level of work to be performed?

- Are laboratory subcontractors adequately insured?

Warranties

- Are there any warranties (expressed or implied) associated with the contract/purchase order? Typical warranties include: (1) quality of materials employed; (2) quality of work performed, e.g., defect free; (3) stipulations that work will conform to the requirements of the contract documents; and (4) stipulations that work will be performed in a certain manner or achieve a certain result.

Limitation of Liability

- Has the contract/purchase order been reviewed for limitations of liabilities, such as duties, damages, and defenses?

- Have certain types of damages, such as defined damages, limited or actual damages, consequential damages, or liquidated damages, been defined?

- Does the contract/purchase order contain a no-damage-for-delay clause, or other schedule-related clauses that limit recovery?

- Is there a contingent payment clause?

- Is liability limited to insurance proceeds that are recoverable?

Contract Default and Termination

- Does the contract/purchase order contain a default or termination clause?

- Does the contract/purchase order contain a notice and opportunity to cure that is clear, concise, and reasonable?

- Are the rights of the terminating party clear, concise, and reasonable?

- Does the contract/purchase order contain a clause for termination for convenience?

- Can wrongful termination be converted to termination for convenience?

- How is compensation determined?

- How are potential damages defined?

- Is there a force majeure clause?

Miscellaneous Requirements

- Does the contract/purchase order contain miscellaneous requirements?

- Are the miscellaneous requirements clearly defined and are they achievable?

It is important to retain all records associated with the contract review process. Additionally, when deviations are noted, the customer must be notified and their approval of the deviation approved. Finally, contract changes received after work has commenced require the same level of scrutiny as the original contract/purchase order.

QUESTIONS TO CONSIDER DURING AN AUDIT

The questions in this section are not intended to be an all-inclusive list to be built into an internal or external audit checklist. However, they are relevant when evaluating the overall effectiveness of a laboratory's contract management.

1. Does the laboratory have an established procedure for the review of requests, tenders, and contracts?

2. Does the review process entail a review of test methods required, alignment of laboratory capabilities, and the determination that customer requirements can be met?

3. Are records of the reviews of requests, tenders, and contracts retained by the laboratory?

4. Does the review include an assessment of the need to outsource testing or calibration work?

5. Are customers notified of deviations from the contract?

6. Are contracts reviewed when amendments to the contract are made?

CHAPTER REVIEW

Understanding customer requirements is a fundamental requirement of ISO/IEC 17025. Customers use a contract or a purchase order to delineate their testing and calibration requirements. Attachments to contracts and purchase orders should contain relevant customer drawings, specifications, and, if applicable, test methods. When it comes to the actual contract review, creating a review checklist that reflects the laboratory's business model is highly recommended. Some final points to remember include: (1) retain all records of the contract/purchase order review process, (2) notify customers and obtain their approval for all deviations, and (3) ensure all customer change orders receive an adequate review.

5

Subcontracting of Tests and Calibrations

Due to the changing needs of the dynamic business environment influencing laboratories, at some point the use of a subcontracting laboratory facility may become necessary. ISO/IEC 17025:2005 recognizes this reality and has identified a few salient requirements associated with the subcontracting of work to other laboratories. As mentioned in Chapter 4, first and foremost, the customer must be notified of intent to subcontract out part or all of the work to another entity. Second, to maintain compliance the laboratory must ensure all offloaded work goes to a competent subcontractor (e.g., a laboratory that is also compliant with ISO/IEC 17025). A point to keep in mind is that all work performed at the subcontractor must be performed in accordance with the requirements of ISO/IEC 17025. In fact, the facility or organization subcontracting the work is responsible for the accuracy and quality of the work. However, if the use of a specific subcontractor is noted in a customer contract, then the customer retains the responsibility for subcontractor performance and general oversight. However, best practice is to take some ownership in the work activities performed by subcontractors even though the selection process is done by someone else. This chapter discusses identification, selection, and use of qualified subcontractors.

Summary of ISO/IEC 17025:2005 Requirement 4.5 (Subcontracting of Tests and Calibrations)

- Laboratories are permitted to outsource work to approved laboratories that comply with ISO/IEC 17025:2005.

- When laboratory work is outsourced, the laboratory must notify the customer in writing. It is strongly recommended that customer approval be obtained in advance.

- The laboratory is responsible for the customer's work performed by a subcontractor, unless the laboratory is directed by the customer to use a specific subcontractor for laboratory testing.

- The laboratory must maintain a record of all subcontractors employed, including evidence of the subcontractor's compliance with ISO/IEC 17025:2005.

EFFECTIVE TOOLS FOR IMPLEMENTATION AND COMPLIANCE

When a laboratory needs to outsource work to another laboratory, the preferred path is to select a laboratory that is already accredited to ISO/IEC 17025. For example, if the laboratory has a valid accreditation certificate from a recognized accreditation body (e.g., the American Association for Laboratory Accreditation, A2LA), then collection of the certificate and completion of a brief questionnaire will suffice (see Figure 5.1). However, if the laboratory selected for outsourcing is not accredited, an on-site evaluation is probably warranted to determine the overall level of compliance with ISO/IEC 17025. The National Institute of Standards and Technology (NIST) website has a complete supplier survey form that can be used to perform a detailed laboratory assessment.

Another important point to remember pertains to responsibilities and customer notification. The laboratory is ultimately

ACME Medical Laboratory Questionnaire—ISO/IEC 17025			
Basic Laboratory Data			
Laboratory name:		Date completed:	
Address: City:　　　　　State/Province:　　　Zip code:　　　Country:			
Telephone number:		Fax number:	
Laboratory Contact Information			
Senior supplier official name:	Title:	Email:	
Senior quality official name:	Title:	Email:	
Senior regulatory official name:	Title:	Email:	
Management representative:	Title:	Email:	
Applicable Certifications (attach copies of all certifications)			
ISO 9001:　　Yes/No　Certificate #:	Exp. date:	Issuing authority:	
ISO 13485:　　Yes/No　Certificate #:	Exp. date:	Issuing authority:	
ISO 17025:　　Yes/No　Certificate #:	Exp. date:	Issuing authority:	
ISO 14001:　　Yes/No　Certificate #:	Exp. date:	Issuing authority:	
FDA-registered facility:　　Yes/No　Registration #:			
List additional certifications (as applicable):			
Business Type			
Public corporation (C-Corp):　Yes/No			
Privately held corporation (C-Corp):　Yes/No			
Limited liability partnership (LLP):　Yes/No			
Laboratory Management Systems (LMS) Questions			
Management Requirements (Section 4)			
1. Does the laboratory have a documented management system?		Yes	No
2. Does the laboratory have an approved quality manual?		Yes	No
3. Does the laboratory have a quality manager and technical manager assigned?		Yes	No
4. Does the laboratory have a written quality policy?		Yes	No

Figure 5.1 Sample questionnaire.

5. Does the laboratory have established quality objectives?	Yes	No
6. Does the laboratory have an established document control procedure?	Yes	No
7. Does the laboratory have an organization chart?	Yes	No
8. Does the laboratory have an established procedure for contract reviews?	Yes	No
9. Does the laboratory outsource testing and calibration work?	Yes	No
10. Does the laboratory have an established procedure for purchasing?	Yes	No
11. Does the laboratory have an established procedure for complaint management?	Yes	No
12. Does the laboratory have an established procedure for nonconforming product?	Yes	No
13. Does the laboratory have an established procedure for corrective action?	Yes	No
14. Does the laboratory have an established procedure for preventive action?	Yes	No
15. Does the laboratory have an established procedure for the control of records?	Yes	No
16. Does the laboratory have an established procedure for internal audits?	Yes	No
17. Does the laboratory have an established policy for management reviews?	Yes	No
Technical Requirements (Section 5)		
18. Does the laboratory have an established procedure for training?	Yes	No
19. Do laboratory employees have written job descriptions?	Yes	No
20. Does the laboratory have an established procedure for environmental controls?	Yes	No
21. Are laboratory environmental conditions routinely monitored?	Yes	No
22. Does the laboratory employ only approved test and calibration methods?	Yes	No
23. Does laboratory have an established procedure for test method validation?	Yes	No
24. Are all methods employed by the laboratory validated prior to their use?	Yes	No
25. Does the laboratory have an established procedure for measurement uncertainty?	Yes	No
26. Does the laboratory have an established procedure for the control of data?	Yes	No
27. Does the laboratory have an established procedure for equipment maintenance?	Yes	No

Figure 5.1   Sample questionnaire. *(continued)*

28. Does the laboratory have an established procedure for measurement traceability?	Yes	No
29. Does the laboratory have an established procedure for the transportation and storage of equipment?	Yes	No
30. Does the laboratory have an established procedure for the handling of test and calibration items?	Yes	No
31. Does the laboratory have an established in-house calibration program?	Yes	No
32. Does the laboratory have an established procedure for quality control in support of monitoring the validity of testing and calibration results?	Yes	No
33. Does the laboratory have an established procedure for issuing test reports and calibration certificates?	Yes	No
QMS Exclusions and Clarifications		
Please list any LMS exclusions:		
Please explain any No answers from Questions 1 through 33:		
Additional comments:		
Name of individual completing this form:		
Title:		
Signature: Date:		
ACME Medical Use Only		
Reviewed by: Accepted: Yes/No Date:		
Signature:		

Figure 5.1 Sample questionnaire. *(continued)*

responsible for the performance of all outsourced work. It is also important to ensure the laboratory's customer is informed (in writing) about work being outsourced. Hopefully, this will be captured during the initial contract review process.

QUESTIONS TO CONSIDER DURING AN AUDIT

The questions in this section are not intended to be an all-inclusive list to be built into an internal or external audit check-list. However, they are relevant when evaluating the overall effectiveness of a laboratory's approach to subcontracting tests and calibrations.

1. Does the laboratory subcontract out to its suppliers test and/or calibration work?

2. Are the suppliers used for subcontracted work in compliance with and/or accredited in accordance with ISO/IEC 17025:2005?

3. Does the laboratory notify customers, in writing, when all or part of their work is outsourced?

4. Does the laboratory maintain an approved supplier's list (ASL) containing the names of qualified subcontractors?

5. Does the laboratory have documented evidence that its subcontractors are either in compliance with or accredited to ISO/IEC 17025:2005?

CHAPTER REVIEW

Outsourcing work to qualified facilities is a perfectly acceptable practice. Although it is always strongly recommended that work be outsourced to an accredited ISO/IEC 17025 laboratory, the minimum requirement is for the facility selected to be in compliance with ISO/IEC 17025. In either case, tools such as questionnaires are available to assist with the selection process. For accredited laboratories, the best practice is to have the subcontractor complete a short supplier questionnaire and provide a copy of the ISO/IEC 17025 certificate. For non-accredited laboratories an onsite evaluation is probably warranted. An important point to remember is that if the decision is made to outsource work, the laboratory assumes responsibility for the quality and integrity of the work performed. Finally, the laboratory must ensure that the customer is notified when the decision is made to outsource even just a small part of a customer's testing or calibration work. It is not only considered best practice, clause 4.5 requires customer notification (in writing).

6

Purchasing Services
and Supplies

Like clause 7.4 of ISO 9001:2008, ISO/IEC 17025:2005 requires laboratories to establish policies and procedures to govern the procurement of critical laboratory supplies and services. Procured supplies used in testing or calibration must be evaluated for fitness of use, typically through inspection upon receipt. Furthermore, the laboratory must retain records of the supplier selection and evaluation process and records associated with the inspection and evaluation of procured supplies and services. Finally, purchase orders and approved material specifications are required for procurement activities. These documents must contain sufficient granularity to ensure the correct supplies or services are being procured and double as a tool that can be employed during the inspection process. This chapter offers a viable approach to the creation and implementation of a purchasing process that complies with ISO/IEC 17025.

Summary of ISO/IEC 17025:2005 Requirement 4.6 (Purchasing Services and Supplies)

- Laboratories must establish policies and procedures that define their purchasing practices, including the procurement, receipt, and storage of materials used for testing and calibration.

- Laboratories must evaluate/inspect procured material, as appropriate, prior to material use.

- Purchase orders and material specifications used to procure laboratory materials must be reviewed and approved prior to their issuance to a supplier.

- Laboratories must perform supplier evaluations of suppliers identified as critical. Records of supplier evaluations shall be retained and an ASL generated.

EFFECTIVE TOOLS FOR IMPLEMENTATION AND COMPLIANCE

The ISO 9001 and ISO 13485 approach to writing procedures for procurement activities is highly recommended. These standards contain significant granularity with regard to fundamental requirements for implementing a successful approach to purchasing and, equally important, selecting, evaluating, and managing suppliers. Although there is no requirement to establish separate procedures, best-in-class laboratories routinely do so. The tools described in this chapter reflect a two-procedure solution.

Supplier Evaluation and Management Procedure

Laboratories must evaluate suppliers of "critical consumables, supplies, and services, which affect the quality of testing and calibration" (ISO 17025, clause 4.6.4). The supplier evaluation process is completely up to the laboratory, provided the approach to supplier evaluation is effective. A common practice employed by laboratories is to use supplier categories to manage the supplier evaluation process (Table 6.1). Additionally, approved suppliers require a listing in an ASL. Purchasing will be tasked with placing orders with qualified suppliers listed in the ASL.

Table 6.1 Typical use of supplier categories.

Supplier category	Requirements	Frequency of audit
Category I Contract laboratories, metrology lab	1. Supplier quality questionnaire on file 2. On-site audit on file 3. No-change agreement on file 4. ISO/IEC 17025 certification on file 5. Listed on ASL	An annual on-site audit is mandatory. Current ISO certificate(s) are collected as part of the audit.
Category II Reagents, testing fixtures, custom components	1. Supplier quality questionnaire on file 2. No-change agreement on file 3. ISO certification on file 4. Listed on ASL Note: On-site audit optional	Supplier quality questionnaire and current ISO certificate(s) are required once every three years.
Category III Commercial off-the-shelf (COTS) equipment and software, consultants	1. Supplier quality questionnaire on file 2. Resumé on file for consultants 3. Listed on ASL Note: ISO certificate on file if available	Supplier quality questionnaire and revised resumés are required once every three years.
Category IV Disposable laboratory aids (e.g., cotton swabs)	No requirements. ASL listing is optional.	N/A

A mail-in survey similar to the one in Chapter 5 (Figure 5.1) can be used for contract laboratories. For other types of suppliers the questionnaire can be modified to reflect an ISO 9001 or ISO 13485 format (see Figure 6.1).

Inevitably, a supplier will provide procured materials or services that are nonconforming; this event will require formal

Supplier Questionnaire			
Basic Supplier Data			
Supplier name:		Date completed:	
Address: City: State/Province: Zip code: Country:			
Telephone number:		Fax number:	
Type of business (e.g., contract manufacturer):			
Supplier classification (ACME Medical use):			
Supplier Contact Information			
Senior supplier official name:	Title:	Email:	
Senior quality official name:	Title:	Email:	
Senior regulatory official name:	Title:	Email:	
Management representative:	Title:	Email:	
Applicable Certifications (attach copies of all certifications)			
ISO 9001: Yes/No Certificate #:	Exp. date:	Issuing authority:	
ISO 13485: Yes/No Certificate #:	Exp. date:	Issuing authority:	
ISO 17025: Yes/No Certificate #:	Exp. date:	Issuing authority:	
ISO 14001: Yes/No Certificate #:	Exp. date:	Issuing authority:	
FDA-registered facility: Yes/No Registration #:			
List additional certifications (as applicable):			
Business Type			
Public corporation (C-Corp): Yes/No			
Privately held corporation (C-Corp): Yes/No			
Limited liability partnership (LLP): Yes/No			
Quality Management System (QMS) Questions			
Quality Management System (Section 4)			
1. Does the organization have a documented quality system?		Yes	No
2. Does the organization have an approved quality manual?		Yes	No
3. Does the organization have a policy for the control of records?		Yes	No
4. Does the organization have a policy for controlling documents?		Yes	No

Figure 6.1   Example of an ISO 9001/13485–style questionnaire.

Management Responsibility (Section 5)		
5. Does the organization hold management reviews?	Yes	No
6. Does the organization have a documented quality policy?	Yes	No
7. Does the organization have an organization chart?	Yes	No
8. Does the organization have a management representative?	Yes	No
Resource Management (Section 6)		
9. Does the organization maintain adequate resources to support the QMS?	Yes	No
10. Does the organization have a documented training program?	Yes	No
Product Realization (Section 7)		
11. Does the organization have a documented policy for design and development?	Yes	No
12. Are design reviews routinely held?	Yes	No
13. Does the organization have a documented policy for procurement?	Yes	No
14. Does the organization maintain an approved suppliers list?	Yes	No
15. Are suppliers routinely audited or monitored?	Yes	No
16. Are all processes validated prior to their use?	Yes	No
17. Does the organization have a policy for identification and traceability?	Yes	No
18. Does the organization perform receiving acceptance activities?	Yes	No
19. Does the organization perform in-process acceptance activities?	Yes	No
20. Does the organization perform final acceptance activities?	Yes	No
21. Does the organization have a documented policy for calibration?	Yes	No
22. Is measuring and monitoring equipment adequately controlled and calibrated?	Yes	No
Measurement, Analysis, and Improvement (Section 8)		
23. Does the organization have a documented policy for internal audits?	Yes	No
24. Are internal audits being performed in accordance with their published schedule?	Yes	No
25. Does the organization have a documented policy for nonconforming material?	Yes	No
26. Does the organization have a documented policy for CAPA?	Yes	No
QMS Exclusions and Clarifications		
Please list any QMS exclusions:		
Please explain any No answers from Questions 1 through 26:		

Figure 6.1   Example of an ISO 9001/13485–style questionnaire. *(continued)*

Additional comments:		
Name of individual completing this form:		
Title:		
Signature:	Date:	
ACME Medical Use Only		
Reviewed by:	Accepted: Yes/No	Date:
Signature:		

Figure 6.1   Example of an ISO 9001/13485–style questionnaire. *(continued)*

corrective action. Supplier-related corrective actions should be split out from the laboratory's CAPA system. Using commercially available software like CATSWeb to manage in-house and external corrective action is an option. However, the use of a supplier corrective action report (SCAR) will suffice (see Figure 6.2). When constructing the SCAR, two categories of SCARs should be created: (1) information only and (2) response required. In some instances informing the supplier of a minor issue is sufficient, so the "information only" category will suffice. If formal corrective action is desired or required, then the "response required" box can be checked.

Depending on the volume of purchase orders being placed, collecting supplier performance metrics to support report cards may be warranted. In any event, supplier performance information should be collected and presented during management review.

Purchasing Procedure

Purchasing must use the ASL to select qualified suppliers. Laboratories are required to create purchase orders and provide drawings and specifications for all services and materials

ACME Medical Data		
Supplier name:	SCAR number:	Date: Due date:
Supplier address:		
Description of problem/condition:		Information only ❏ Response required ❏
Supplier Analysis		
Remedial action pursued:		Due date:
Root cause analysis:		Due date:
Completed by:	Title:	Date:
Corrective action taken:		
Completed by:	Title:	Date:
ACME Medical SCAR Review and Closure		
Did supplier provide adequate evidence of effectiveness of actions taken: ❏ Yes ❏ No Comments:		
SCAR status: ❏ Closed		Date:
Reviewed by:	Signature:	

Figure 6.2 Example of a SCAR.

procured. Purchase orders can take many forms and are usually driven by the needs of the business (Figure 6.3). A no-change clause or agreement is recommended as part of the purchase order or as a stand-alone document. Additionally, purchase orders and associated documentation must be reviewed and approved before issuance. Change orders should also be issued

Purchase Order

ABC Company
1234 Progress Parkway
Anytown, USA 54545

Purchase Order 00000000012345	Date 10/10/2013	Page 1	
Payment Terms Net 30	**Freight Terms** FOB	**Ship via** Best method	
Requestor	**Department** XYZ Company	**Location** T0500	**REQ ID** 00006789

Ship To: Receiving
500 Business Circle
Big City, USA 12345

Bill To: Accounts Payable
500 Business Circle
Big City, USA 12345

Line-Sch	Quantity	Item/Description	Unit Price	Extended Amt	Due Date
1–1	50	EA Solenoid valves	200.00	10,000.00	12/05/2013

Subtotal: $ 10,000.00

Sales Tax: $ 0.00
Freight: $ 50.00
Misc. Charge: $ 0.00

TOTAL: $10,050.00

This order must comply with the General Provision Committee bylaws for goods, services, or information technology acquisitions. Vendor shall comply with all safety standards as required by law.

NOTE: Any change or modification in terms, quantities, or specifications may be made without express authorization by the Committee. No other office or employee may authorize changes.

CERTIFICATION AND APPROVAL OF PURCHASE ORDER
I hereby certify on my own knowledge that this order for the purchase of the items specified is issued in accordance with the procedure described by law governing such items, and that all such legal requirements have been met.

By: _____
Title: _____
Tel: _____ Fax: _____

Figure 6.3   Example of a purchase order.

to document all changes to requirements noted after the initial purchase order has been placed.

Evaluation of Purchased Materials and Services

One final requirement that needs to be addressed as part of the procurement process is the evaluation of procured materials or services. Incoming inspection is a salient requirement needed to ensure procured materials and services conform to the requirements of the purchase order and applicable drawings and specifications. Records collected as part of the inspection process, including the inspection methods employed, must be retained and managed in accordance with the laboratory's record control procedure.

QUESTIONS TO CONSIDER DURING AN AUDIT

The questions in this section are not intended to be an all-inclusive list to be built into an internal or external audit checklist. However, they are relevant when evaluating the overall effectiveness of the laboratory's purchasing procedure.

1. Does the laboratory have an established procedure that governs the selection of suppliers and the procurement of supplies and services?

2. Does the laboratory perform acceptance activities (testing and/or inspection) on procured materials?

3. Does the organization use purchase orders with sufficient granularity to procure supplies and services?

4. Does the laboratory have an established procedure to evaluate suppliers?

5. Are records of supplier evaluations being maintained?

CHAPTER REVIEW

Activities associated with purchasing, supplier evaluation, and evaluation of procured services and materials must be governed by established procedures. It is imperative that services and materials be purchased using purchase orders that are supported by drawings and specifications. Additionally, purchase orders must be placed only with suppliers listed on the laboratory's ASL that have been appropriately evaluated and approved. Once purchased services or materials have been received, they must be evaluated against the purchase order and supporting documentation for fitness for use. Furthermore, if the procured material or service is deemed to be nonconforming, the nonconformance should be documented and a SCAR issued to the supplier. Finally, all activities associated with purchasing, supplier evaluation, and the inspection of procured materials and services must be documented and the records retained.

7

Service to the Customer

Customer focus and customer service have been a target of multiple ISO standards for many years. ISO/IEC 17025:2005 is no exception. The key word with regard to ISO/IEC 17025 is "cooperation." Laboratories are not only expected to cooperate, they must also provide their customers information in a timely fashion. Customers must be granted access to the laboratory when requested. In some cases, the visit may be to facilitate an annual verification audit or to witness a particular test or calibration. Additionally, the laboratory should always be proactive and seek feedback, both positive and negative, from its customers. Customer feedback is a valuable tool in helping organizations assess the performance of their management system, which in turn drives performance improvements in the testing and calibration services provided. This chapter focuses on the fundamentals of providing service to the customer in a laboratory environment.

Summary of ISO/IEC 17025:2005
Requirement 4.7 (Service to the Customer)

- Laboratories must cooperate with customers and facilitate customer requests for monitoring testing and/or calibration.

Note: This cooperation includes: (1) customer access for witnessing testing and/or calibration and (2) activities such as preparation and packaging as required by customers to support verification activities.

- Laboratories need to actively pursue critical customer feedback to drive improvement of the management system, including testing and calibration activities.

Note: Customer satisfaction surveys are excellent tools for obtaining customer feedback (positive and negative).

EFFECTIVE TOOLS FOR IMPLEMENTATION AND COMPLIANCE

The first requirement associated with clause 4.7 is laboratory accessibility. Accessibility is always a concern for laboratories, especially if some of the test or calibration activities can be classified as proprietary in nature. In some cases, the work being performed may be categorized as classified (typically associated with defense contracts). Despite these concerns, laboratories must make every effort to facilitate visits from customers wanting to witness testing or calibration. In fact, visiting and witnessing work being performed at least once per year is a good practice. This activity could coincide with an annual audit of the laboratory, another strongly recommended practice.

The second requirement associated with clause 4.7 is the need to solicit feedback from customers. Maintaining an open line of communication between the service provider and customer is critical to fostering a good business relationship. When creating a survey to solicit customer feedback there are three points to consider:

- Be clear about the purpose of the survey
- Be specific about the questions asked

- Ask a lot of questions, but not to the point where the survey becomes burdensome

Another important point to remember is that different surveys are used to obtain specific kinds of customer feedback. For example, a customer satisfaction survey is used to gauge a laboratory's performance of a specific task or over a specific time period. A marketing survey is used to query customers about specific needs or the potential to expand laboratory capabilities. A customer loyalty survey seeks to determine if customers are considering a move to a competitor. Figure 7.1 shows an example of a simple customer satisfaction survey.

One final type of customer feedback worth mentioning is the customer complaint. Customer complaints, which will be discussed in detail in Chapter 8, should never be taken lightly. When a customer complaint is received, contacting the customer and attempting to discover the underlying reason for the complaint is always a best practice.

QUESTIONS TO CONSIDER DURING AN AUDIT

The questions in this section are not intended to be an all-inclusive list to be built into an internal or external audit checklist. However, they are relevant when evaluating the overall effectiveness of a laboratory's customer service.

1. Does the laboratory have an established procedure that delineates its approach to customer service?

2. Does the laboratory grant reasonable access to the laboratory and the test and calibration areas when requested by a customer?

3. Does the laboratory actively seek feedback from its customers?

Dear Customer:

As the customer service manager of [Laboratory], I want to thank you for giving us the opportunity to serve you. Please help us serve you better by taking a couple of minutes to tell us about the service that you have received so far. We appreciate your business and want to make sure we meet your expectations. Attached, you will find a coupon good for ...... We hope that you will accept this as a token of our goodwill.

Sincerely,

[MANAGER_NAME]

What laboratory service are you currently using?

❏ Calibration
❏ Testing
❏ Calibration and testing

How often do you use our laboratory services?

❏ Daily	❏ Once per month
❏ Once or more per week	❏ Every two to three months
❏ Two or three times per month	❏ Two or three times per year

Overall, how satisfied are you with our laboratory's service?

❏ Very unsatisfied	❏ Very satisfied
❏ Unsatisfied	❏ Extremely satisfied
❏ Somewhat satisfied	

How likely are you to use our laboratory again?

❏ Definitely	❏ Probably not
❏ Probably	❏ Definitely not
❏ Might or might not	❏ Never used

Would you recommend our laboratory services to others?

❏ Definitely	❏ Probably not
❏ Probably	❏ Definitely not
❏ Might or might not	❏ N/A

What recommendations would you offer for improving our laboratory's service?

Thank you for your feedback.

Figure 7.1 Customer satisfaction survey.

4. When feedback (positive or negative) is received from a customer, how is this information used to drive continuous improvement?

5. Does the laboratory use customer surveys to seek feedback?

CHAPTER REVIEW

This chapter makes two important points: (1) laboratories need to facilitate reasonable accommodations for customers wishing to witness testing and calibration activities, and (2) effective customer communication and the solicitation of feedback is not only a fundamental requirement of clause 4.7, it is necessary to support good business relationships. Finally, complaints, which are considered a type of customer feedback, should never be taken lightly. Contacting the customer and discovering the underlying reason(s) behind the complaint is a best practice.

8

Complaints

D ealing with a complaint from a customer is never pleasant. Unfortunately, laboratories are not immune from
customer complaints. ISO/IEC 17025:2005 requires
laboratories to establish a policy supported by a well-written
procedure to delineate the process of addressing customer
complaints, including the investigative process and subsequent
corrective action. Although complaints typically have negative
connotations, world-class organizations have the ability to use
critical feedback from the customer to improve performance
and turn a customer complaint into an event with a positive
outcome. The key is to treat each complaint event proactively, while striving to resolve the concerns of the customer.
This chapter will review proven methods used by organizations to manage customer complaints and comply with ISO/
IEC 17025:2005 requirements.

Summary of ISO/IEC 17025:2005
Requirement 4.8 (Complaints)

Laboratories must establish a policy and procedure to handle
complaints. As part of the complaint management process,
records of complaints, complaint investigations, and corrective
actions pursued in support of complaint mitigation must be
retained.

EFFECTIVE TOOLS FOR IMPLEMENTATION AND COMPLIANCE

Customer complaints are never pleasant. Regardless of fault, customers believe they are always in the right. This perception makes the handling of a customer complaint all the more challenging. Many different tools can be used to assist with the complaint mitigation process. Regardless of the approach pursued, complaint management needs to be a closed-loop process. Figure 8.1 shows an example of a closed-loop feedback process. The steps in the closed-loop feedback process are: (1) collect data, (2) take action, (3) communicate feedback, and (4) refine changes.

Step 1: Collect Data

All relevant data must be collected. A good source of data is similar complaints from other customers or information gleaned from customer satisfaction surveys, a topic of Chapter 7. If the complaint information collected is insufficient, contacting the customer to obtain as much useful information as possible is helpful.

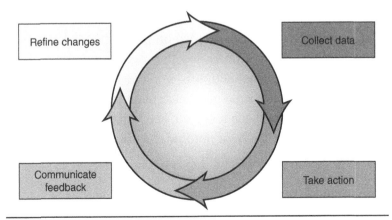

Figure 8.1 Four-step closed-loop process.

Step 2: Take Action

Collecting the data is not enough. Once collected, the data must be properly analyzed and, hopefully, a conclusion drawn as to the root cause of the complaint. If the data are inconclusive, revisit the "collect data" step. Tools such as the 8 Disciplines of Problem Solving and DMAIC (define, measure, analyze, improve, control) are useful when employed as part of the investigative process.

Step 3: Communicate Feedback

Once the complaint investigation has been completed, communicating the results of the investigation to the customer is important. Even inconclusive results of the root cause analysis should be communicated to the customer. However, in that case, work should continue to determine the root cause. Typically, failure to identify the root cause is a sufficient reason to open up a formal corrective action request (CAR) to further diagnose the cause(s) behind a complaint. If the "take action" step results in a definitive root cause, share the results with the customer along with a sincere promise to prevent recurrence of the problem.

Step 4: Refine the Changes

If the first three steps are executed properly, the final step is to implement the changes necessary to prevent recurrence of the complaint. Until formal action is implemented and effectiveness is verified, there is no guarantee that the issue causing the initial complaint has been resolved. Having a repeat complaint, after the customer has been notified that the problem has been resolved, will be a game changer.

Formalized Process

Addressing complaints needs to be a formalized process. Clause 4.8 of ISO/IEC 17025 requires laboratories to establish

Complaint Form
Customer complaint number: Date opened: Nature of the complaint: Name of complainant: Phone number: Complainant address:
Complaint received by: Title: Date received: By: ❏ Visit   ❏ Phone   ❏ Letter   ❏ Sales   ❏ Credit memo   ❏ Other
Complaint Issue ❏ Testing accuracy: ❏ Missing certificate of conformance: ❏ Missing certificate of calibration: ❏ Equipment received damaged: ❏ Other (specify):
Received by QA manager: Date: Assigned to: Response due: Instructions: Distribution: ❏ Quality control   ❏ Engineering   ❏ Production   ❏ Sales
Analysis CAPA required: ❏ Yes ❏ No   CAR number: **Evaluation** Date(s) evaluation performed: Evaluation results:
Action/Reply to Customer ❏ None. Reason for no action: ❏ Replaced   ❏ Repaired   ❏ Credit   ❏ Letter sent   ❏ Sales follow-up
Final Disposition   Reviewed by QA: Date: Reviewed by Engineering: Date: Reviewed by Regulatory: Date:

Figure 8.2   Sample complaint form.

a policy and written procedure outlining the complaint management process. It is essential that a complaint form be created to support the complaint process. Although the complaint form will be tailored to the specific laboratory environment, all complaint forms have many similarities. Figure 8.2 shows a generic complaint form for a laboratory environment.

QUESTIONS TO CONSIDER DURING AN AUDIT

The questions in this section are not intended to be an all-inclusive list to be built into an internal or external audit checklist. However, they are relevant when evaluating the overall effectiveness of a laboratory's complaint management system.

1. Does the laboratory have an established procedure to manage complaints?

2. Are customer complaints thoroughly investigated?

3. When the results of an investigation indicate the need for corrective action, is corrective action actively pursued?

4. Are records of complaints being maintained by the laboratory?

CHAPTER REVIEW

No organization likes to receive negative feedback. However, such feedback should be treated as a gift. Chances are good that other customers are unhappy, and a complaint may be the only chance to address and correct a problem. The key is to be proactive. Not only does the customer expect a root cause analysis to prevent future problems, he or she wants to be kept informed. If the results of an investigation are inconclusive, communicate that result to the customer. However, work toward determining the root cause should continue. One final thought before closing out this chapter: If a laboratory does not take care of its customer base, rest assured another laboratory will step in and gladly fill the role.

9

Control of Nonconforming Testing and/or Calibration Work

It is inevitable that at some point a nonconforming event will impact a test or calibration performed by a laboratory. Clause 4.9 of ISO/IEC 17025:2005 offers laboratories a blueprint for dealing with nonconformances identified during the execution of testing and calibration services. A nonconformance can fall into two categories: (1) nonconformity with a laboratory's internal procedures and methods or (2) a failure to meet a customer-specified requirement. In either case, once a nonconformance has been identified, the standard requires immediate and decisive action to resolve the problem. The laboratory must investigate the nonconformance, determine the appropriate action (accept the nonconformance or repeat testing), notify the customer if such notification is deemed appropriate, and pursue formal corrective action to prevent recurrence. This chapter explores a proactive approach to managing nonconformance in a laboratory environment.

Summary of ISO/IEC 17025:2005 Requirement 4.9 (Control of Nonconforming Testing and/or Calibration Work)

- Laboratories must establish a policy and procedure for managing nonconforming testing and/or calibration when such events occur. At a minimum, the policy and procedure shall address:

—Management responsibilities and authority for managing nonconforming events

—Evaluation of the nonconforming event

—Corrective actions pursued

—Disposition of the testing and/or calibration work identified as nonconforming

—The customer notification process, including the recall of nonconforming work

—Management's responsibility to authorize resumption of work

- If the results of the investigation into the nonconforming event indicate that a recurrence is possible, laboratories must pursue formal corrective action in accordance with clause 4.11 of ISO/IEC 17025:2005.

EFFECTIVE TOOLS FOR IMPLEMENTATION AND COMPLIANCE

Like other requirements delineated within ISO/IEC 17025, the management of nonconforming testing and calibration requires the establishment of a procedure. Readers who are familiar with the management of nonconforming products in the traditional sense, such as in support of an ISO 9001 QMS, will recognize many similarities. However, establishing a stand-alone procedure to manage nonconforming testing and calibration rather than combining it with another procedure is always considered a best practice.

Some elements that must be incorporated into the laboratory's procedure are:

- Clear definitions of the roles and responsibilities of all laboratory personnel tasked with handling nonconforming testing and calibration

- Detailed assessment of the nonconforming work and/or activity

- Pursuit of immediate corrective action

- A decision process for determining the acceptability of nonconforming work and/or activity

- A customer notification process

- The recall of nonconforming work

- A process for authorizing the resumption of work and/or activity

Depending on the nature of the nonconformance, formal corrective action may be warranted. If formal corrective action is required, clause 4.11 (covered in Chapter 11 of this book) should be used for guidance.

Two important pieces of documentation are needed to assist with the identification and documentation of a nonconforming test or nonconforming calibration. These are the nonconforming report (NCR) tag (Figure 9.1) and the NCR form (Figure 9.2). For example, once a piece of equipment associated with a nonconforming calibration event is identified, an NCR tag should be affixed to it and the instrument quarantined. The form documenting the nonconforming calibration should be filled out at the same time. As previously stated, if formal corrective action is required or the nonconformance took place

Date NCR opened:_____ NCR number:_____

Test/Calibration number:_____ S/N:_____

Description:_____

Comments:_____

Figure 9.1 Example of an NCR tag.

Nonconforming Testing or Calibration Information				
Test/calibration number:	Test description/calibrated instrument:	NCR #:		Date:
Customer name:	PO #:	Date received:	Date:	Date rejected:

Nonconformance type: ❏ Testing   ❏ Calibration   ❏ Other

Item	Specification	Description of nonconformance	Test or calibration

Originator name:	Signature:	Date:

Disposition

❏ Accept—No problem found   ❏ Rework/repeat
❏ Rework/repeat test   ❏ Return to:

Responsibility: ❏ Laboratory   ❏ Contract laboratory

Item	Disposition code	Instructions/Comments

QA name:	Signature:	Date:
Engineering name:	Signature:	Date:
Customer service name:	Signature:	Date:

Closeout

Corrective action required: ❏ Yes ❏ No	CA:
Supplier notification: ❏ Yes ❏ No	SCAR #:
Customer notification: ❏ Yes ❏ No	Date:

QA name:	Signature:	Date:

Figure 9.2   Example of an NCR form.

in work outsourced to another laboratory, the form can capture the corrective action decision.

QUESTIONS TO CONSIDER DURING AN AUDIT

The questions in this section are not intended to be an all-inclusive list to be built into an internal or external audit checklist. However, they are relevant when evaluating the overall effectiveness of a laboratory's control of nonconforming testing and calibration work.

1. Does the laboratory have an established procedure that governs the handling of nonconforming testing and calibration results?

2. Does the procedure define the responsibilities of laboratory personnel tasked with the review and disposition of nonconforming work?

3. Are formal investigations pursued for nonconforming testing and calibration work?

4. What is the laboratory's process for correcting nonconforming work?

5. If nonconforming work has been shipped to a customer, what is the process for recalling the nonconforming work?

6. Is the customer notified of all nonconformances affecting their test or calibration?

7. How is the customer notified?

8. Who in the laboratory has the authority to allow the work to continue?

9. If the investigative process shows that a nonconformance has the potential to recur, is formal corrective action pursued to remediate the potential for recurrence?

CHAPTER REVIEW

Laboratories must pursue immediate action when a nonconforming test or calibration is noted. The remediation process may require the notification of the customer and the recall of nonconforming test articles or pieces of equipment. Ensuring that nonconforming testing and calibration events find their way into the laboratory's corrective action system is a best practice. Corrective action is the best way to prevent a nonconforming test or calibration from recurring. Finally, nonconforming testing and calibration events need to be thoroughly documented with an NCR form. Whenever possible, the material associated with a nonconforming test or any nonconforming instrumentation associated with a calibration should be identified and quarantined.

10

Improvement

Continuous improvement is a fundamental goal of proactive organizations. W. Edwards Deming, Kaoru Ishikawa, and Genichi Taguchi dedicated their lives to developing tools to assist organizations in striving for continuous improvement and the implementation of effective, quality-driven tools. The requirements in clause 4.10 of ISO/IEC 17025:2005 reinforce the spirit of these quality pioneers by requiring laboratories to assess the effectiveness of the laboratory's management system. At a minimum, laboratories must use a well-written quality policy, clearly defined quality objectives, results of internal and external audits, corrective actions, preventive actions, and management reviews to drive continuous improvement. Proactively seeking customer feedback can also enhance a laboratory's pursuit of improvement. This chapter will discuss valuable tools for driving continuous improvement activities while supporting compliance with ISO/IEC 17025:2005.

Summary of ISO/IEC 17025:2005 Requirement 4.10 (Improvement)

Laboratories must invest in the continuous improvement of their management system. Tools deployed by the laboratory in support of management system improvement are: (1) the quality policy, (2) quality objectives, (3) audits (internal and external), (4) data analysis, (5) CAPA, and (6) management review.

EFFECTIVE TOOLS FOR IMPLEMENTATION AND COMPLIANCE

Clause 4.10 is a catch-all clause that reinforces the need for laboratories to use all available tools to improve their management system. It is simply not enough to publish a quality policy, assemble and publish a few quality objectives, pursue corrective and preventive actions, perform a critical assessment of collected data, or hold an annual management review. Improvement is the sum of multiple elements required by ISO/IEC 17025. Since most of these requirements are inputs into an effective management review, specific requirements delineated in clause 4.10 should be included in the management review agenda. However, since the information is vital to effective laboratory management, reviewing this information annually is insufficient to drive real-time laboratory improvement.

Quality Policy

The quality policy, although reflective of the laboratory's operating policies and principles, is typically cast in stone. However, laboratories need to revisit it regularly and adjust it to reflect the current business environment. Laboratory employees must also receive training in the quality policy, including its meaning. Best practice is to retrain to the quality policy annually. This can be accomplished through an all-hands meeting.

Quality Objectives

The laboratory's quality objectives should be set early in the fiscal year. All laboratory personnel should be aware of the objectives, and the objectives should be posted throughout the laboratory. Quality objectives should be reasonable and supported by collectible and objective metrics. Best practice is to update quality objective results at least monthly.

Audits (Internal and External)

Progress against an internal audit schedule and the results of internal audits are fairly easy to track. Nonconformances identified during internal audits should be loaded into the CAPA system. External audits are a little more subjective because input is coming from customers and regulatory bodies. However, the feedback coming from external audits should be treated as valuable advice that can be used to drive improvement of the management system. Nonconformances identified by external audits should definitely be loaded into the CAPA system.

Data Analysis

Information critical to the effective operation of the laboratory needs to be collected and analyzed for trends. For example, collected data associated with customer complaints, nonconforming testing or calibration, supplier corrective action requests, and so forth should be analyzed to ensure performance expectations are being achieved. Without the collection and analysis of critical data, ascertaining the effectiveness of ongoing laboratory operations is nearly impossible.

CAPA

CAPA, when properly employed, is an effective tool to drive improvement. In fact, the CAPA program drives the adjustments necessary to improve the effectiveness of the management system. When in doubt, it is always best to ensure CAPA is pursued for audit nonconformances, unfavorable data trends, nonconforming tests, nonconforming calibrations, and customer complaints.

Management Review

Management reviews are held at least annually. Although management review is a mandatory requirement, because of the annual schedule most laboratories adhere to, its value as a tool is limited. The primary purpose of a management review is for senior management to review and gauge the overall effectiveness of the management system in the preceding 12-month period. Senior management may request that formal corrective action be assigned and pursued if concerns over the performance of the management system are noted.

QUESTIONS TO CONSIDER DURING AN AUDIT

The questions in this section are not intended to be an all-inclusive list to be built into an internal or external audit checklist. However, they are relevant when evaluating the overall effectiveness of a laboratory's improvement activities.

1. Does the laboratory strive to continuously improve the management system?

2. What tools does the laboratory use to drive improvement?

3. Are improvement activities included in the management review?

CHAPTER REVIEW

Compliance with clause 4.10 is based on multiple requirements delineated in ISO/IEC 17025. The expectation is that laboratories use multiple tools and metrics to collect performance data associated with ongoing laboratory operations and use the subsequent data analysis to identify trends. When trends reveal performance issues with the laboratory's management system, the laboratory needs to pursue CAPA to implement corrections and improvements. Internal audits and external audits can also provide valuable insight into the effectiveness of the management system. Using all available tools to create a proactive environment to drive management system improvements is a best practice.

11

Corrective Action

An organization's ability to correct nonconformances is a cornerstone of a QMS. As with ISO 9001:2008, documenting policies and procedures for corrective action is an important requirement of ISO/IEC 17025:2005. While establishing a systemic approach to corrective action, inputs to consider are: (1) nonconforming work, (2) deviations from audits (internal and external), (3) customer feedback (typically complaints), and (4) observations made by laboratory employees. Another important influencer of a laboratory's approach to corrective action is the ability to frame the problem and to work diligently toward the identification of the root cause. Correcting the root cause of nonconformances will be difficult in the absence of an effective and exhaustive approach to root cause analysis. Once the root cause has been determined and corrective actions implemented, these actions must be monitored for effectiveness. If necessary, follow-up audits should be planned to preclude future nonconformances. The elements required for an effective corrective action system will be discussed in this chapter.

Summary of ISO/IEC 17025:2005 Requirement 4.11 (Corrective Action)

- Laboratories must establish a policy and written procedure that describes all activities associated with corrective action. The laboratory must ensure sufficient authority is granted to a designee who will manage corrective action and act on behalf of management with regard to decisions made.

- Corrective action requires a thorough investigation to determine root causes.

- When corrective action is deemed necessary, the laboratory will propose corrective actions and implement accordingly. Corrective actions should be selected based on whether they will resolve the original problem and preclude the recurrence of similar problems. All corrective actions must be documented.

Note: Corrective actions must be appropriate to the risk.

- Laboratories must verify the effectiveness of corrective actions.

- When nonconformances are identified and corrective actions pursued, laboratories must perform additional audits, as deemed necessary and premised on elevated business risk, to maintain compliance with ISO/IEC 17025:2005.

EFFECTIVE TOOLS FOR IMPLEMENTATION AND COMPLIANCE

Laboratories must establish a policy and procedure to ensure an effective approach to corrective action is pursued. As part of the policy and procedure, the laboratory must designate an individual responsible for oversight of the corrective action process. Several software options are available commercially that can help to meet the requirements in clause 4.11 of ISO/IEC 17025. For example, CATSWeb is a software product dedicated to a proactive approach to corrective action. If a laboratory is not inclined to spend money on a software solution, another option is to use basic software products such as Microsoft Word and

Excel with secured and password-protected access to oversee the corrective action process.

A critical part of the corrective action process is ascertaining the root cause of a problem. Tools are available to assist in the performance of root cause analysis. Ishikawa's seven basic quality tools are frequently used to support failure investigations. These tools include: (1) cause-and-effect diagrams, (2) check sheets, (3) control charts, (4) histograms, (5) Pareto charts, (6) scatter diagrams, and (7) stratification. Regardless of the approach pursued, the expectation set in ISO/IEC 17025 is that a reasonable attempt must be made to determine root causes.

When a laboratory has determined that corrective action is required to mitigate a nonconformance, the corrective action, including the assessment of risk, must be appropriate to the problem. When corrective action has been selected, all proposed changes must be documented, reviewed, and approved prior to implementation. An area to consider when procedures change is training. Laboratory personnel must be retrained, as appropriate, when procedures change. In most cases, the retraining will be as simple as reviewing and understanding changes to a procedure. Regardless of the level and detail of training required, the training should be documented.

Another important piece of the corrective action process is the verification of effectiveness (VOE). A laboratory must not only verify that corrective action has been formally implemented, but the laboratory must also verify that the corrective action taken was effective. Depending on the type of corrective action taken, the verification process should occur within 30, 60, or 90 days. The VOE is rarely performed immediately. Once the VOE has been successfully completed, then, and only then, can the corrective action be closed.

Figure 11.1 shows an example of a corrective action form. The same form can also be employed for preventive action, the topic of Chapter 12. Figure 11.2 shows an example of a

Originator Data		
Name:	❏ Corrective action ❏ Preventive action	Date:
Subject:		
Description of problem/condition:		
Quality Assurance Review		
❏ Rejected Reason for rejection:		
❏ Approved Immediate action required (containment):		Due date:
Assigned to:	Department:	CAPA #:
Corrective Action/Preventive Action		
Analysis of root cause:		Date:
Corrective action/preventive action plan:		Due date:
Corrective action/preventive action taken:		Date completed:
Reviewed by:		Date:
Quality Assurance Follow-Up/Verification of Effectiveness		
Provide documented evidence of CAPA implementation/effectiveness:		
Corrective/preventive action notice status: ❏ Closed		Date:
Reviewed by:	Signature	

Figure 11.1   Example of a CAPA form.

CAPA number	Date opened	CAPA owner	Target date for CAPA closure	Date root cause complete	Date CAPA plan complete	Date corrective action implemented	Date VOE performed	Date CAPA closed
12-001	1/21/12	J. Doe	4/21/12	1/26/12	1/28/12	2/4/12	3/4/12	3/5/12
12-002	2/23/12	S. Smith	5/23/12	3/10/12	3/12/12	3/15/12	5/15/12	5/16/12
12-003	6/10/12	R. Jones	9/10/12	7/1/12	7/15/12	7/31/12		
12-004	6/25/12	R. Jones	9/25/12	7/15/12	8/1/12			

Figure 11.2 Example of CAPA log sheet.

corrective action log sheet that can be used concurrently with the corrective action form.

One final thought relates to performing additional audits, as required, to ensure that the nonconformances identified and the subsequent corrections implemented do not cause potential compliance issues. Adjusting the internal audit schedule may be necessary to ensure problems requiring corrective action receive additional oversight so that nonconformances cease to manifest themselves in the laboratory. The internal audit program (discussed further in Chapter 14) should be flexible enough to add additional audits, as required, to ensure ongoing laboratory compliance with its own policies, procedures, regulatory and statutory requirements, and ISO/IEC 17025.

QUESTIONS TO CONSIDER DURING AN AUDIT

The questions in this section are not intended to be an all-inclusive list to be built into an internal or external audit checklist. However, they are relevant when evaluating the overall effectiveness of a laboratory's corrective action program.

1. Does the laboratory have an established policy and procedure for corrective action?

2. Does the corrective action procedure require inputs from: (a) nonconforming work, (b) noncompliances with policies and procedures, (c) internal audits, (d) external audits, (e) customer complaints/feedback, and (f) employee observations?

3. Does the corrective action process require root cause analysis?

4. Is there evidence that adequate corrective actions are being pursued?

5. Is VOE being performed for all corrective actions?

6. Is there a master log sheet for corrective actions?

7. Are all corrective actions current?

8. Are follow-up audits performed when required?

CHAPTER REVIEW

Corrective action is an extremely important tool to mitigate nonconformances while ensuring the laboratory continues to comply with internal policies and procedures, regulatory and statutory requirements, and ISO/IEC 17025. ISO/IEC 17025 requires key pieces of information regarding the corrective action process. At a minimum, the procedure must include: (1) root cause analysis, (2) identification of proposed corrective action, (3) corrective action implemented, (4) VOE, and (5) the need for additional audits. The laboratory must perform a thorough job of determining the root cause of nonconformances. Without a clearly defined root cause, implementing effective corrective action becomes an impossible task. Ample time should be allowed to elapse prior to performing the VOE, as it may take a few months before changes made to a procedure can adequately be assessed for effectiveness. One final thought is to remember that the ultimate goal is to achieve and sustain ISO/IEC 17025 accreditation. It is important to avoid shortcuts when establishing the management system. Compliance with all aspects of the standard, regardless of whether the requirement is written or implied, is mandatory.

12

Preventive Action

Preventive action is often viewed as a gray area. However, ISO/IEC 17025:2005 is very prescriptive with regard to framing a definition for preventive action. According to ISO/IEC 17025, preventive action drives organizational improvements and identifies potential sources of nonconformities before such potential nonconformities can negatively affect the laboratory. The laboratory cannot simply identify potential opportunities for preventive action; it must act. Laboratories must draft preventive action plans, implement preventive action plans, and monitor the effectiveness of preventive action activities. This chapter presents a proactive approach to managing preventive actions in support of achieving and sustaining compliance with clause 4.12 of ISO/IEC 17025:2005.

Summary of ISO/IEC 17025:2005 Requirement 4.12 (Preventive Action)

- When a laboratory identifies necessary improvements or potential sources of nonconformities, preventive action must be pursued, including the creation of action plans. The goal of preventive action is to ensure laboratories reduce the likelihood of nonconforming events.

- Laboratories must establish a procedure to manage preventive action. At a minimum, the procedure should include: (1) the initiation of preventive action activities and (2) applicable monitoring tools to ensure preventive actions pursued are effective.

Note: Preventive action should be considered a proactive process used to pursue opportunities for organizational improvement.

EFFECTIVE TOOLS FOR IMPLEMENTATION AND COMPLIANCE

In Chapter 11, Figure 11.1 shows an example of a form that can be used to document corrective action as well as preventive action. Preventive action is often overlooked by organizations because problems often manifest so quickly that they move straight into corrective action. ISO/IEC 17025 requires laboratories to establish a procedure for preventive action. Although not required, combining the corrective action and preventive action requirements into one procedure makes good sense. Essentially, the steps taken for preventive action mirror the requirements for corrective action.

The Preventive Action Process

The fundamental goal of preventive action is to avoid nonconformances. Identification and mitigation of potential nonconformances is rooted in three basic concepts: (1) the identification of risk, (2) the identification of potential deficiencies, and (3) the prioritization of solutions to drive improvement. There is no better tool to illustrate these concepts than the failure mode and effects analysis (FMEA). Table 12.1 shows an example of a

Table 12.1 FMEA example.

	Function	Failure type	Potential impact	Severity	Potential causes	Occurrence	Detection mode	Detection	Risk priority number
Definition	Brief summary of the function	Describe the failure mode	Describe the potential impact of the problem	How severe is the effect?	What are the potential causes?	What is the frequency of occurrence?	What are the existing controls for detection?	How easy is the failure to detect?	Risk priority number
Example	Control of the mechanical lab temperature	Temperature is out of tolerance	Incorrect calibration values obtained	3	HVAC system failure	1	Temperature chart recorder	2	6

generic FMEA. These points need to be considered when constructing an effective FMEA:

- The FMEA must drive design or process improvements as its primary objective.

- The FMEA must address all high-risk modes identified.

- The FMEA must consider all lessons learned, internal and external to the laboratory.

- The FMEA must identify key characteristic candidates, as appropriate.

- The FMEA should always be completed when it provides the most value and not after a nonconformance has occurred.

- The FMEA requires input from subject-matter experts to ensure its content is adequate.

- The FMEA should always be thoroughly completed.

- The FMEA process should always be evaluated for effectiveness.

Improvement projects supported by project plans are another approach to effective preventive action. When creating a project plan to support an improvement project, elements to be considered are:

- Clear definition of the actions to be taken

- A definitive timeline for each activity

- Assignment of a resource to each activity

- Project reviews and status reports that delineate progress

- Clear channels of communication to disseminate project information

- A formal review and closeout of each improvement project and plan

QUESTIONS TO CONSIDER DURING AN AUDIT

The questions in this section are not intended to be an all-inclusive list to be built into an internal or external audit checklist. However, they are relevant when evaluating the overall effectiveness of a laboratory's preventive actions.

1. Does the laboratory have an established procedure for preventive actions?

2. Are preventive action plans developed when opportunities for improvement are identified?

3. Are records of preventive action maintained by the laboratory?

CHAPTER REVIEW

Combining the corrective action requirement and the preventive action requirement into one procedure is a perfectly acceptable approach. In fact, because the steps involved in pursuing successful preventive action mimic those of corrective action, including the CAPA form, placing the two requirements together into one procedure makes sense. Many tools are available to support the preventive action process, but the FMEA is probably the best choice for the job. FMEAs, when properly constructed, are extremely powerful. Depending on the nature of preventive action and the potential impact on a laboratory, the pursuit of an improvement project, supported by a project plan and team, can be a viable alternative. In either case, pursuing effective preventive action is always a laboratory's best defense in avoiding nonconformances.

13

Control of Records

Effective control of records is a salient requirement for organizations operating in a regulated environment. Like ISO 9001, ISO 13485, and AS9100, ISO/IEC 17025:2005 has specific requirements related to the control and management of records. The requirements in clause 4.13 are prescriptive and require an established procedure that covers: (1) record identification, (2) record collection, (3) record indexing, (4) record access, (5) record filing, (6) record storage, (7) record maintenance, (8) record disposal, (9) quality records, and (10) technical records. Records exist in various media; however, for most organizations, records are in a hard-copy format (paper) or an electronic format (e-file). In any case, laboratories must implement adequate systems to preserve and retain records in accordance with regulatory, statutory, and customer requirements. First and foremost, the records must be protected and secured to preserve confidential content. Implementing good documentation practices (GDP) is paramount when establishing effective record control. Records must always be accurate; if errors are made, these errors must be corrected. This chapter discusses the control and preservation of records, the establishment of a table for record retention for quality and technical records, the implementation of GDP, and tools needed to support ISO/IEC 17025 compliance.

Summary of ISO/IEC 17025:2005 Requirement 4.13 (Control of Records)

Control of Records

• Laboratories must establish a written procedure to control and maintain all records (quality and technical).

• Records must be legible and stored in a manner that protects them from damage, deterioration, and loss. Records must be easy to retrieve.

Note: In accordance with ISO/IEC 17025:2005, records can be any form of media.

• Records must be secure and their confidentiality protected.

• Laboratories must have an established procedure to back up electronic records and prevent unauthorized access to electronic records.

Technical Records

• Laboratories must retain technical records that document all testing and calibration activities. The records need to contain sufficient granularity to support an audit trail. Calibration records should capture: (1) factors influencing measurement uncertainty, (2) the names of laboratory personnel performing work, (3) observations, and (4) related calibration data.

Note: It may not be possible to retain records of all observations, but every effort should be made to do so.

Note: ISO/IEC 17025:2005 categorizes technical records as a collection of data. Examples of technical records are forms, test reports, and calibration certificates.

• Data must be recorded at the time of collection and linked to a specific task (test or calibration step).

• When errors or mistakes are made or noted, they must be corrected using GDP. GDP consists of the crossing out of incorrect data and the addition of correct data, supported by the date and the initials of the person making the correction.

EFFECTIVE TOOLS FOR IMPLEMENTATION AND COMPLIANCE

Because of the significant importance ISO/IEC 17025 places on record legibility, record retention periods, protection of records from deterioration, record security, data accuracy, reports, GDP, certifications, and electronic records, a laboratory must establish a procedure with sufficient granularity to manage its records. As part of the procedure development process, laboratories should consider: (1) general requirements, (2) record storage, (3) record retention periods, (4) GDP, (5) packaging and identification of records, (6) indexing of archived records, (7) shipment of records, (8) storage accessibility and security of records, and (9) record inspection and audits.

General Requirements

All laboratory records must be maintained internally or at an approved off-site storage facility. Laboratory records must be readily available to laboratory personnel, customers, and regulatory bodies upon request. Laboratory records must also be adequately protected from deterioration. When deemed necessary, adequate security measures should be employed to protect confidential customer records.

Record Storage

All records must be legible and stored in appropriate filing containers to minimize deterioration and loss. Records stored electronically need to be backed up on a regular basis.

Record Retention Periods

The procedure must specify retention periods for quality records and technical records. A table should be created listing each laboratory record and its retention period. Table 13.1 shows an example of such a table. Record retention periods

Table 13.1 Sample document matrix for a laboratory.

Document name	Record type	Maintained by	Retention period (minimum)
Approved Suppliers List	Quality	Quality	3 years
Audit Checklist (Internal)	Quality	Quality	2 years
Audit Reports	Quality	Quality	2 years
Calibration Certificates	Quality	Quality	3 years
Calibration Procedures	Technical	Technical	5 years
Calibration Records/Data	Technical	Technical	5 years
Complaint Form	Quality	Customer Service	3 years
Complaint Log	Quality	Customer Service	Permanently
Component Specifications	Technical	Technical	7 years
Contracts/Modifications	Quality	Sales	Permanently
Controlled Environment Monitor Log	Technical	Quality	5 years
Corrective Actions	Quality	Quality	7 years
Customer Drawings	Technical	Document Control	7 years
Engineering Change Order	Quality	Document Control	5 years
External Audit Records	Quality	Quality	5 years

should be linked to regulatory, statutory, and customer retention requirements.

GDP

Laboratories must implement GDP when it comes to corrections and revisions made to records.

Packaging and Identification of Records

When records are stored off site, they must be properly identified to facilitate their retrieval. Off-site storage facilities such as Iron Mountain are able to provide guidance in support of the packaging and identification of records.

Indexing of Archived Records

The laboratory must index all records processed for archival storage. Laboratories must audit archived records to verify the accuracy and integrity of the archived records process.

Shipment of Records

The laboratory will need to coordinate the movement of records to be archived and act as liaison with the storage provider.

Storage Accessibility and Security of Records

All archived records must be stored with a provider that will protect the integrity of the records and ensure protection from unauthorized access. Additionally, when external facilities are chosen for record storage, the record storage areas need to be maintained in a manner that prevents the deterioration and loss of records.

Record Inspection and Audits

Annual record inspection and audits should be scheduled as part of the internal audit program. The purpose of an annual record inspection and audit is to ensure that the archival record storage areas adequately protect the safety, integrity, and security of the records.

QUESTIONS TO CONSIDER DURING AN AUDIT

The questions in this section are not intended to be an all-inclusive list to be built into an internal or external audit

checklist. However, they are relevant when evaluating the overall effectiveness of a laboratory's control of records.

1. Does the laboratory have an established procedure to control records?

2. Does the procedure address identification, collection, indexing, access, filing, storage, maintenance, and disposal of quality and technical records?

3. Does the procedure contain a record retention requirement (length of record retention)?

4. Are records legible?

5. Are records stored in a suitable environment capable of protecting them?

6. Are records properly secured so as to protect their confidentiality?

7. Does the laboratory have an established procedure for the storage of electronic records?

8. Does the established procedure for storage of electronic records contain a process for backup, security, and access to electronic records?

9. When mistakes are made in records, does the laboratory use GDP to correct the errors?

CHAPTER REVIEW

Maintaining the integrity of records is a mission-critical endeavor for laboratories. The procedure established to control records must contain sufficient granularity to ensure they are accurate, legible, preserved, stored in adequate conditions, and readily retrievable. If an off-site storage contractor is used as part of the laboratory's control of records policy, annual audits of the record storage facility must be performed. If records are stored electronically, a process for maintaining electronic media must be included in the procedure, including daily backups of electronic files. Finally, retaining records forever is impractical. A record retention table must accompany the record control procedure. Record retention periods should be linked to regulatory, statutory, and customer retention requirements.

14

Internal Audits

Internal audits, when properly implemented, are proactive tools for assessing an organization's ongoing compliance with a standard or regulation. Like ISO 9001:2008, ISO/IEC 17025:2005 requires laboratories to periodically conduct internal audits to verify laboratory operations are performed in accordance with established policies and procedures and with ISO/IEC 17025. Specifically, the internal auditing program must ensure that all aspects of the management system are evaluated. Audits should be planned and a schedule created and published to support the internal auditing program. Laboratory personnel tasked with performing audits must be trained and qualified. When deviations are noted during the performance of internal audits, corrective action should be pursued to remedy the nonconformance. This chapter describes how to implement an effective internal audit program, including the creation of a viable schedule.

Summary of ISO/IEC 17025:2005 Requirement 4.14 (Internal Audits)

- Laboratories must schedule and perform internal audits to ensure ongoing operations are performed in accordance with the documented management system and in compliance with

ISO/IEC 17025:2005. Internal audits must address all elements of the management system, including testing and calibration activities.

Note: The internal audit cycle is one year.

- If problems are noted during the execution of audits, laboratories are required to pursue corrective action.

- The results of internal audits must be recorded.

- When applicable, follow-up audits must be performed to verify the effectiveness of corrective actions. These activities must be recorded.

EFFECTIVE TOOLS FOR IMPLEMENTATION AND COMPLIANCE

As stated in Chapter 10 and noted as a requirement in clause 4.10, internal audits are a valuable tool for driving management system improvements in a laboratory. Performing timely internal audits and, when warranted, re-audits of laboratory functional areas that are identified as problematic is crucial. First and foremost, laboratories must establish an internal auditing program documented by a written procedure. All elements of the laboratory's management system must be assessed at least once annually. When corrective action opportunities are identified, the effectiveness of the corrections must be verified. The results of internal audits need to be documented and retained as a quality record.

An internal auditing schedule should be assembled and approved prior to the start of each year. This schedule should be published and qualified auditors assigned in advance. *Note:* ISO 19011:2011 (Guidelines for Auditing Management Systems) should be reviewed prior to establishing an internal auditing program and auditor requirements. Figure 14.1 shows a typical internal auditing schedule based on a quarterly format.

Department/Area	Primary element(s)						Q1	Q2	Q3	Q4	Auditor
Organization	4.1						X				Smith
Management system	4.2						X				Smith
Document control	4.3	4.3.1	4.3.2	4.3.3			X				Smith
Review of requests, tenders, and contracts	4.4						X				Jones
Subcontracting of tests and calibrations	4.5							X			Jones
Purchasing services and supplies	4.6							X			Smith
Service to customer	4.7							X			Rogers
Complaints	4.8							X			Rogers
Control of nonconforming testing and/or calibration work	4.9								X		Smith
Improvement	4.10								X		Smith
Corrective action	4.11	4.11.1	4.11.2	4.11.3	4.11.4	4.11.5			X		Jones
Preventive action	4.12								X		Jones
Control of records	4.13	4.13.1	4.13.2	4.13.3						X	Rogers
Internal audits	4.14									X	Smith
Management reviews	4.15										Rogers

Figure 14.1 Example of an internal auditing schedule.

This schedule can be modified to a monthly format. Another option is for the laboratory to subcontract the internal auditing function to a qualified auditor or consulting firm.

Having a certified auditor, although preferred, is not a requirement of ISO 19011. However, auditors must be appropriately trained and have adequate technical knowledge of the function or process they are auditing. Auditors must never have functional responsibility for the areas they are auditing to prevent bias. Auditor objectivity and independence are crucial for the performance of an internal audit.

Components of an Internal Audit

Successful execution of an audit is much more than having the auditor show up with a pencil and a pad of paper. A good audit takes planning and preparation to ensure it is effective and beneficial to the laboratory. Many components are associated with an internal audit. Depending on the size of the laboratory, some of the components may be skipped or greatly reduced in scope.

Audit Planning

Prior to executing the audit, the auditor must become familiar with the area to be audited. The audit plan typically covers the scope, purpose statement, area/function to be audited, list of audit team members (if applicable), and the relevant documents. Depending on the scope of the audit and on whether multiple functional areas are being audited, it may be prudent to develop an audit agenda to support the plan. An audit checklist (see Figure 14.2) should also be created to support the internal audit. To save time on the day of the audit, the auditor should request and review relevant documents in advance.

Opening Meeting

The opening meeting is a useful tool for establishing the boundaries of the audit, reviewing the audit plan, reviewing the audit

Date of internal audit: _____   **Lead auditor:** _____

Auditee: _____   **Area audited:** _____

Function audited: Organization, management, and personnel	Yes	No	N/A	Comment
Is a laboratory organizational chart or other information available listing staff organization and responsibilities? Does it identify the QA officer and all the relationships between the QA officer, technical operations, and support staff?				
If the laboratory is part of a larger organization, are there any organizational arrangements that could cause a conflict of interest?				
Does the laboratory have a health and safety program in place for all employees?				
Does the laboratory have policies or procedures or procedures to ensure client confidentiality and proprietary rights, including procedures for protecting the electronic storage and transmission of results?				
Do the laboratory managerial and technical personnel have the authority and resources needed to carry out their duties, to identify departures from the quality system, and procedures for performing environmental tests, and to initiate actions to prevent or minimize such departures?				
Are the education and technical background of all personnel documented?				
Does the QA officer have the authority to stop work and initiate action to prevent or minimize quality system variances?				
Is there a formal QA manual in place and does the QA officer maintain the current quality manual?				

Figure 14.2   Example of an internal audit checklist.

agenda, and discussing other issues influencing the audit. The dynamics of the audit, including the closing meeting, should be reviewed at this time. A sign-in sheet should be used to document attendance at the opening meeting.

Performing the Audit

Executing the audit is nothing more than carrying out the audit plan. If a checklist has been created for the audit, use it as a guide. The checklist can be used to collect objective evidence of compliance and assist the auditor during the interview process. However, it is important to remember that the audit report will be the primary source of objective audit evidence.

Collecting and Documenting Evidence

During the audit, collecting objective evidence related to document compliance and nonconformances, if applicable, is important. Evidence is needed to document nonconformances identified during the audit. Additionally, evidence of compliance is needed to support the audit report.

Audit Nonconformances

If the audit reveals a nonconformance with a policy, procedure, standard, or regulation, the nonconformance must be documented. When documenting the nonconformance, specifying the requirement (e.g., ISO/IEC 17025:2005, clause 4.15, Management Review) and the finding (no evidence of management reviews being performed) is important. The nonconformance documentation should always be clear, concise, and objective.

Closing Meeting

Like the opening meeting, the closing meeting may be deemed optional, depending on the size of the organization. If a closing meeting is held, an attendance sheet should be circulated to capture attendance. During the closing meeting the auditor presents the audit results. Highlighting the positives is as important as noting nonconformances. If a follow-up audit is required, it should be noted during the closing meeting along with next steps to mitigate nonconformances.

Audit Report

The audit report is a detailed written summary of the internal audit. A written report should be completed within seven days of the audit but must be completed no later than 30 days after the audit.

Corrective Action

Nonconformances identified during the audit must be corrected. Depending on the nature and severity of the nonconformance (e.g., systemic), formal corrective action may need to be pursued. Simple corrections can be performed, and the auditor can document the corrections in the audit report.

Verifying Effectiveness of Corrective Action

The VOE of audit corrections typically occurs during the next audit cycle. However, if the audit nonconformance is systemic and the nonconformance has been moved to the laboratory's CAPA system, VOE will be performed as part of CAPA. Even if the VOE is performed as part of CAPA, the individual selected to perform the next audit must verify that the nonconformance has been closed and the action taken was effective.

QUESTIONS TO CONSIDER DURING AN AUDIT

The questions in this section are not intended to be an all-inclusive list to be built into an internal or external audit checklist. However, they are relevant when evaluating the overall effectiveness of a laboratory's internal audit.

1. Does the laboratory have an established procedure that governs the internal auditing program?

2. Is there a published audit schedule?

3. Are internal audits performed in accordance with the published schedule?

4. Does the laboratory use auditors who have been properly trained or certified in the performance of audits?

5. When nonconformances are identified, does the laboratory pursue corrective action to resolve them?

6. Is the audit schedule adjusted when evidence indicates that a functional area within the laboratory requires additional oversight?

7. Is the effectiveness of corrections resulting from internal audits being verified?

8. Are records maintained for internal audits?

CHAPTER REVIEW

Internal audits are tools that drive ongoing improvements in the laboratory's management system. In order for the internal auditing program to be effective, it must be well documented by procedure and an annual internal auditing schedule must be created, reviewed, approved, and published. Audits require proper advance planning and trained auditors capable of executing internal audits. Multiple components are associated with an internal audit. An audit plan must be supported by an agenda (if applicable) and an audit checklist must be created to assist in the facilitation of each audit. Finally, when nonconformances are identified during an audit, corrective action must be pursued to correct all nonconformances noted.

15

Management Reviews

Organizations use management reviews to ensure the management system remains effective. Included in the management review process, which should be held at least once per year, is the collection of quality records and records that capture the ongoing effectiveness of testing and calibration activities. Clause 4.15 of ISO/IEC 17025:2005 contains specific metrics to be reported as part of the management review process. Like the management review inputs associated with ISO 9001:2008, ISO/IEC 17025 requires the results of audits, customer feedback, and recommendations for improvement to be included in management review meetings. Management reviews must be well attended, the results recorded in detailed meeting minutes, and, when deemed appropriate, outcomes of the management review, including corrective action, documented. When actions are assigned, management is responsible for ensuring that corrective actions are actively pursued and completed. This chapter presents best-in-class management review practices, including the creation of the agenda and sign-in sheet.

Summary of ISO/IEC 17025:2005 Requirement 4.15 (Management Reviews)

- Laboratories must establish a procedure for management reviews. Management reviews must be scheduled and held to ascertain the effectiveness of the laboratory's management system and of the testing and calibration work being performed, including the effectiveness of corrective action when the results of management reviews indicate that improvements are necessary. Items to include in the management review process are:

  —Ongoing effectiveness of procedures

  —Manager and supervisor reports

  —Audit results (internal and external)

  —CAPA

  —Results of comparison and proficiency testing performed by the laboratory

  —Analysis of work composition, including changes in mix and volume

  —Feedback received from customers

  —Customer complaints

  —Recommendations received to drive laboratory improvements

  —Other business relevant to the effective operation of the laboratory (e.g., resources)

Note: Ideally, management reviews should occur at least once per year. Additionally, management review outputs should support laboratory planning, goals, and objectives.

- Management reviews, including action items identified, must be documented. Management is responsible for ensuring action items are completed within the allotted time period.

EFFECTIVE TOOLS FOR IMPLEMENTATION AND COMPLIANCE

A management review is a valuable management tool to ensure the laboratory's management system and technical tools are adequate and performing as expected. It is a generally accepted practice to perform management reviews at least annually; however, more frequent reviews will improve laboratory performance further. Although monthly management reviews are considered a best practice, quarterly reviews are also effective and economically viable.

When establishing the procedure for management review, ISO/IEC 17025 requires specific elements to be included in the procedure:

- A review of action items assigned during previous management review meetings

- An assessment of suitability of ongoing policies and procedures

- Reports from supervisors and managers

- Internal audit results

- CAPA activities pursued

- The results of external audits

- The results of interlaboratory comparisons and proficiency tests

- Changes in work volume and mix

- Customer feedback

- Customer complaints

- Recommendations for improvement

- Relevant activities being pursued and metrics being collected

Management reviews must include six components to be successful: (1) a published schedule for management reviews, (2) an agenda for each management review, (3) a sign-in sheet for the management review meeting, (4) the actual management review meeting, (5) the management review meeting minutes, and (6) a link to CAPA in case the management team assigns corrective action based on the data/results presented in the management review meeting.

Published Management Review Schedule

The schedule for management reviews must be published at the beginning of each year. If the management review is held once annually, then the process is as simple as stating that the management review will be held in a specific month, e.g., January. If reviews are held quarterly, reviews can be scheduled for the month following the close of a quarter. Because the laboratory owns the management system, the review schedule is based on the laboratory's schedule. *Note:* If a quorum is not available to attend the management review, rescheduling the meeting is acceptable. However, such rescheduling should be documented.

Management Review Meeting Agenda

To ensure consistency in the management review agenda, the agenda items should be prepared in advance and should align with the minimum requirements in clause 4.15 of ISO/IEC 17025. Listing the agenda items as inputs and outputs in the management review procedure is considered a best practice. Doing so reduces the risk of omitting information that is relevant to the ongoing performance of the management system from the management review. Figure 15.1 shows an example of a simple management review agenda.

Date:

To: All ISO/IEC 17025:2005 Process Owners

Subject: Management Review Meeting

Please plan to participate in our Formal Management Review Meeting on [Day, DD Month YYYY], from [Start Time] to [End Time] in the [Location].

We will be addressing quality-related topics for this meeting specifically prescribed, as a minimum, within the ISO 9001:2008 Standard, as follows:

Agenda
- A review of action items assigned during previous management review meetings
- An assessment of ongoing suitability of policies and procedures
- Reports from supervisors and managers
- Internal audit results
- CAPA activities pursued
- The results of external audits
- The results of interlaboratory comparisons and proficiency tests
- Changes in work volume and mix
- Customer feedback
- Customer complaints
- Recommendations for improvement
- Relevant activities being pursued and metrics being collected

To help you prepare for our meeting, copies of or intranet links to the following materials are being provided with this agenda:

- Copies of reports for Internal Audits completed since the last Management Review Meeting
- The most recent Customer Feedback Report and Summary of Warranty Returns
- The most recent Summary of Outgoing Product Conformity Data
- Summary of Corrective and Preventive Action Requests initiated and pending since the last Management Review Meeting
- Minutes from the prior Formal Management Review Meeting
- Previously established Quality Objectives
- Our Quality Management System Manual, which contains our current Quality Policy
- Proposed new Quality Objectives, indicating how each directly supports our Quality Policy and our organization's strategic business plan

In order to comply with the ISO/IEC 17025:2005 Standard the following meeting outcomes are required and will be necessary to document, along with an attendance record:

1. Improved effectiveness of our QMS/processes;
2. Improved product related to customer requirements; and
3. An assessment of current resource needs.

Figure 15.1 Example of a management review agenda.

Management Review Sign-in Sheet

Because of the confidential nature of the information, management review meeting content does not have to be shared with laboratory customers or regulatory bodies, such as the FDA. However, evidence that the meetings take place is required. A sign-in sheet containing the name, function, and actual signature of each attendee is required. If a member of the management team is not in attendance, sending an alternate is acceptable. However, if more than 50% of the management team is absent, the meeting should be rescheduled.

Management Review Meeting

There is no industry standard for the duration of a management review meeting. The meeting should be long enough to present, review, and discuss each agenda item. Although it is not always practical, holding the management review meeting off site may reduce the number of interruptions, resulting in a more fruitful meeting.

Management Review Meeting Minutes

One individual should be assigned the task of taking notes and assembling them into the management review meeting minutes. Typically, the assignment is given to a member of the quality organization. Having the meeting minutes reviewed and published as quickly as possible is important. There is no industry standard regarding the time period for issuing meeting minutes; however, seven days is a realistic goal. It should never take longer than 30 days to publish the minutes.

Management Review Corrective Actions

From time to time, management may decide that further actions are required to ensure the management system complies with ISO/IEC 17025. The action requested by management could be somewhat simple and be handled informally (although still documented). However, typically actions resulting from management review require formal corrective action. If formal corrective action is required, the request for action coming out of management review should be placed into the CAPA system. It is much easier to track assigned actions in the CAPA system than to use an informal approach. In either case, actions taken must be reviewed during the next management review. This shows how management oversight tends to lose some effectiveness when reviews are held annually.

QUESTIONS TO CONSIDER DURING AN AUDIT

The questions in this section are not intended to be an all-inclusive list to be built into an internal or external audit checklist. However, they are relevant when evaluating the overall effectiveness of the laboratory's management review process.

1. Does the laboratory have an established procedure for management reviews?

2. How often are management reviews held?

3. Is the schedule for management reviews published?

4. What information is presented and reviewed during management reviews?

5. Do outputs from management reviews feed into the CAPA system when the reviews dictate that corrective action is required to address an issue?

6. Does a sign-in sheet reflect attendees of management review meetings?

7. Does the laboratory maintain records of management reviews?

CHAPTER REVIEW

Establishing a procedure and holding at least one management review per year are mandated by ISO/IEC 17025. However, the more frequent the management reviews, the more effective the management review process tends to be. As for management review content, an agenda is strongly recommended. Agenda items can be included in a procedure to drive consistency in the management review process. An attendance sheet documents attendance and can be used as evidence that the management review meetings are being held. If a quorum is not available to attend the management review, the meeting should be rescheduled. However, rescheduling the meeting too many times can result in nonconformance with a regulatory body that governs management effectiveness. Meeting minutes should be posted as soon after the management review meeting as possible. Finally, if the management team decides corrective action is required based on meeting inputs, the corrective action process is better served by loading the request into the CAPA system. Finally, the status of assigned actions should be reviewed in the next management review meeting.

PART II

Technical Requirements

16

Technical Requirements—General

Clause 5.1 of ISO/IEC 17025:2005 migrates away from the management system and quality requirements associated with the standard and begins to address the technical requirements needed to ensure the testing and calibration practices are robust. As stated in clause 5.1, multiple factors influence the accuracy of the work performed and the measurements obtained by laboratories, including: (1) human factors, (2) environmental conditions, (3) test methods (including test method validation), (4) equipment, (5) measurement traceability, (6) the approach to measurement sampling, and (7) the handling of test and calibration items. Laboratories must consider these elements when writing test procedures and generating test and calibration methodologies. The qualifications and training of laboratory personnel must also be considered when test methods and calibration methods are established.

Summary of ISO/IEC 17025:2005 Requirement 5.1 (Technical Requirements—General)

- Many factors influence the accuracy, reliability, and repeatability of laboratory testing and calibration. Significant influencers deserving consideration are:

  —The influence of human factors

  —The influence of environmental conditions in the laboratory

—The influence of test method validation practices

—The influence of laboratory equipment used for testing and calibration

—The influence of measurement traceability on calibration work

—The influence of sampling plans (created and/or employed)

—The influence of handling test samples and equipment submitted for testing or calibration

- All these factors can affect measurement uncertainty. Laboratories must ascertain the extent of their influence and take it into consideration during the development of testing and calibration methodologies.

EFFECTIVE TOOLS FOR IMPLEMENTATION AND COMPLIANCE

Clause 5.1 identifies influencers of measurement uncertainty. Laboratories must identify all factors that can affect the accuracy of testing and calibration. Each of these elements needs to be thoroughly understood and monitored. Subsequent chapters in this book will break down the requirements needed by laboratories to provide accurate and repeatable test and calibration results. Although clause 5.1 does not require an established procedure, a simple procedure that acknowledges the requirement and contains pointers to where these elements can influence measurement uncertainty is recommended.

- Personnel factors (clause 5.2) will be addressed in Chapter 17.

- Accommodation and environmental conditions (clause 5.3) will be addressed in Chapter 18.

- Test and calibration methods and method validation (clause 5.4) will be addressed Chapter 19.

- Equipment (clause 5.5) will be addressed in Chapter 20.

- Measurement traceability (clause 5.6) will be addressed in Chapter 21.

- Sampling (clause 5.7) will be addressed in Chapter 22.

- The handling of test and calibration items (clause 5.8) will be addressed in Chapter 23.

QUESTIONS TO CONSIDER DURING AN AUDIT

The questions in this section are not intended to be an all-inclusive list to be built into an internal or external audit checklist. However, they are relevant when evaluating the overall understanding of a laboratory's technical requirements.

1. Does the laboratory consider all factors that can influence the testing and calibration work?

2. Do the evaluation factors include: (a) human factors, (b) environmental conditions, (c) test methods (including test method validation), (d) equipment, (e) measurement traceability, (f) the approach to measurement sampling, and (g) the handling of test and calibration items?

CHAPTER REVIEW

Laboratories must identify and monitor all elements in the laboratory that can influence the accuracy of testing and calibration work. All factors influencing measurement uncertainty must be adequately explored and their influence understood. Laboratories are not required to establish a procedure to address the requirements delineated within clause 5.1 of ISO/IEC 17025; however, a brief procedure that provides pointers to each of the elements of uncertainty is recommended.

17

Personnel

At the core of any successful organization are the people that support day-to-day operations. Experience, skill, education, and training are salient elements to consider when working toward compliance with the personnel requirements in clause 5.2 of ISO/IEC 17025:2005. Appropriate levels of competency must be established for each function within the organization. Additionally, adequate supervision must be provided during the initial training of personnel until each employee reaches required competency levels. As a laboratory grows, the training program and supervisory personnel must expand to ensure employees keep pace with the ongoing evolution of technology. Laboratories wishing to achieve or retain ISO/IEC 17025 accreditation must sustain continuous improvement opportunities, driven by a highly skilled and well trained employee base.

Summary of ISO/IEC 17025:2005 Requirement 5.2 (Personnel)

The laboratory management team is responsible for ensuring the overall competence of employees. This includes training employees to ensure they have or achieve a specific level of competence to execute their duties. Close supervision is required until employees achieve competence. Education, training, and experience are critical elements that laboratory management must consider when determining employee competence.

In some cases, certification may be required for laboratory personnel responsible for performing highly technical tasks.

Specific requirements are delineated for laboratory personnel who write test reports and/or the explicit opinions presented in test reports. Laboratory employees tasked with writing reports and opinions must:

- Be qualified and knowledgeable about the technologies employed

- Have relevant and applicable training

- Have sufficient and relevant experience

- Know applicable standards, including regulatory ones

- Understand the significance of noted deviations and the influence such deviations have on the actual testing results

Laboratory management must establish a written policy/ procedure for training. At a minimum, the training program needs to address: (1) applicable education, (2) applicable training, (3) applicable skill set(s), and (4) verification of training effectiveness. The training program will also be applicable to contract labor and consultants employed by a laboratory.

Current job descriptions are also an important requirement for laboratory personnel. Although there is some flexibility in the development of job descriptions, some fundamental elements need to be considered, such as:

- Specific laboratory responsibilities must be clearly defined

- Level of required technical expertise needs to be defined

- Level of experience needs to be defined

- Specific technical qualifications need to be defined

- Relevant training requirements need to be defined

- Managerial and supervisor responsibilities (including reporting structure) need to be defined

- Educational prerequisites should be defined

Laboratories are responsible for managing and retaining training records for all laboratory personnel, regardless of their functional responsibilities or technical expertise.

EFFECTIVE TOOLS FOR IMPLEMENTATION AND COMPLIANCE

A basic requirement for laboratories working toward accreditation or sustaining accreditation is the establishment of a documented policy/procedure that indicates the training requirements for all laboratory personnel. Employee training and competence drive the overall quality and performance of the laboratory. Laboratories are expected to ensure all personnel have the appropriate level of skill, experience, education, and training to execute testing and calibration activities. In some instances, specific technical training may be required, e.g., for operating a scanning electron microscope. This additional training could be based on an industry standard or a regulatory/statutory certification requirement. Additionally, laboratory personnel who interpret testing results or write test reports must possess:

- Relevant industry or technical knowledge concerning the materials tested or the actual performance of a specific test

- An appropriate level of knowledge of applicable standards and regulatory/statutory requirements

- A thorough understanding of noted deviations associated with the materials tested and the overall testing process

An important tool in support of meeting the training requirement is a training matrix. The training matrix helps laboratory management to define and manage training requirements for all laboratory personnel, including contract labor. The training matrix should include: (1) training to validated test methods, (2) training to industry standards such as ASTM, (3) training to quality system procedures, (4) training to applicable sections of ISO/IEC 17025, and (5) training to applicable regulatory and statutory requirements. Figure 17.1 shows an example of a basic training matrix.

Although the training matrix is a viable tool for managing the big picture of the laboratory's training, additional detail is required. Documentation of training is also required for all

ACME Test Labs Training Matrix 5.2 of ISO/IEC 17025:2005	ASTM A370	ASTM D1708	ASTM D256	QPM0001	QSP0001	ISO/IEC 17025	ISO 9001	TM0002	21 CFR Part 820
Version/Section	−12	−10	−10	A	A	2005	2008	B	820.72
Employee									
J. Doe 1	X			X	X	X	X	X	
J. Doe 2	X			X	X	X		X	
J. Doe 3	X	X	X	X	X	X		X	X
J. Doe 4			X	X	X	X			
J. Doe 5			X	X	X	X			
J. Doe 6		X		X	X	X	X		X
J. Doe 7		X	X	X	X	X			X
J. Doe 8	X	X	X	X	X	X		X	X

Figure 17.1   Sample training matrix.

laboratory personnel. Each employee should have an individual training file, regardless of job function. The individual employee training records should contain documented evidence of previous and relevant training, current training, certifications, applicable education, and evidence of competency testing (if deemed appropriate). Additionally, best-in-class training records for laboratory personnel will contain a resume and a job description. A well-written job description supports the overall training requirement for laboratory personnel.

Unlike ISO 9001, which does not include a requirement for a job description, 5.2.4 of ISO/IEC 17025 does require laboratories to write and maintain job descriptions for laboratory personnel. There is some latitude granted with regard to job description content; however, there are minimum requirements for defining responsibilities for management, technical personnel, and key support personnel. For example, each job description should define responsibilities:

- As they pertain to performing tests and calibrations

- As they pertain to planning tests and calibrations

- As they pertain to evaluating test results

- As they pertain to generating reports that state opinions and interpretations of the test and calibration results

- As they pertain to test method validation activities

Additionally, expertise and experience required, qualifications, training programs, and managerial-specific duties must be included in the job description. Figure 17.2 shows an example of a well-written job description.

QUESTIONS TO CONSIDER DURING AN AUDIT

The questions in this section are not intended to be an all-inclusive list to be built into an internal or external audit

ACME Test Labs

Laboratory Quality Manager Job Description   JD0001, REV A—08/08/12

1.0 Primary Job Function
The Laboratory Quality Manager is responsible for the laboratory's Quality Management System (QMS) and QMS implementation in accordance with ISO/IEC 17025. The Laboratory Quality Manager retains direct access to executive management, at which decisions are made in regard to laboratory policies, resources, practices, and direction provided to the laboratory's technical manager.

2.0 Education and Skills
The Laboratory Quality Manager is required to possess the following education, experience, and skills:

* Bachelor of Science Degree in a scientific/engineering field;
* A minimum of 10 years of experience in a laboratory environment;
* Proficiency in MS Word, Excel, Access, PowerPoint, and Project software; and
* Competency in employing the principles associated with ISO/IEC 17025 and ISO 9001.

3.0 Authority
The Laboratory Quality Manager reports directly to the president of ACME Test Labs and retains the authority to:

* Approve deviations from established procedures;
* Evaluate and determine the validity of customer complaints;
* Evaluate and resolve calibration-related nonconformances;
* Review laboratory calibration results;
* Open corrective and preventive actions; and
* Issue certificates of conformance.

4.0 Responsibilities
The Laboratory Quality Manager is responsible for:

* Performing employee training as it relates to the QMS;
* Maintenance of the Quality Policy Manual;
* Managing the Internal Quality Audit Program;
* Entertaining audits for clients and regulatory bodies;
* Managing the CAPA program;
* Managing the QMS;
* Ensuring only approved documentation is released for use by ACME personnel;
* Managing the customer complaint process;
* Supplier selection and evaluation;
* Preparing the documentation for management review meetings; and
* Other duties and responsibilities deemed appropriate in support of sustaining quality operations at ACME Test Labs.

5.0 Training Requirements
* QPM0001—ACME Quality Policy Manual
* QSP0002—ACME Quality Policy
* QSP0006—ACME Purchasing Services and Supplies
* QSP0008—ACME Customer Complaints
* QSP0011—ACME Corrective Action
* QSP0012—ACME Preventive Action
* QSP0014—ACME Internal Audits
* QSP0015—ACME Management Reviews

Figure 17.2   Example of an ISO/IEC-compliant job description.

checklist. However, they are relevant when evaluating the over-all effectiveness of a laboratory's training program.

1. Does the laboratory have a documented training program?

2. Does the training procedure address the goals and requirements for specific levels of education, training, experience, and demonstrated skill?

3. Who is responsible for identifying the training needs of the laboratory?

4. Is there a requirement for verifying if the training performed is effective?

5. Does the training procedure address the requirement for supervision of employees in training?

6. Does the laboratory have and maintain training records for all employees?

7. Who is responsible for managing employee training records?

8. Is there an annual review process for training?

9. Does the laboratory have written job descriptions for all employees?

10. Are the job descriptions current?

CHAPTER REVIEW

Training is a fundamental requirement to ensure a laboratory is capable of providing repeatable and accurate quality testing and calibration services. Establishing a written procedure that delineates the content of the training program is a basic requirement of ISO/IEC 17025. The creation of a training matrix is a sound practice that allows a laboratory to quickly ascertain the training status of laboratory personnel; however, the training requirement is more expansive than just the matrix. All laboratory personnel should have a training file, regardless of function or responsibilities. The training file will contain all training-related documentation needed to support claims of compliance with clause 5.2 of ISO/IEC 17025. Each employee must also have a detailed job description—a requirement that differs from ISO 9001, which does not specifically require job descriptions. A well-written job description will support the laboratory's training program. One final thought for the reader is to remember that the ultimate goal is to achieve and sustain accreditation to ISO/IEC 17025. The best advice is not to take shortcuts when establishing the management system. Compliance to all aspects of the standard, regardless of whether the requirement is written or implied, is mandatory.

18

Accommodation and Environmental Conditions

Like the infrastructure and work environment clauses in ISO 9001:2008, clause 5.3 of ISO/IEC 17025:2005 includes specific requirements related to maintaining a proper laboratory environment. Laboratories must establish and maintain environmental conditions appropriate for the testing and calibration work being performed. They must ensure that environmental conditions never have an adverse effect on the results of testing and calibration. Not only is the establishment of a suitable laboratory environment required, but the laboratory must monitor, control, and record environmental conditions that are relevant to the performance of the test method and calibration methods used. Specific requirements to consider are: (1) biological factors (sterility), (2) dust, (3) electromagnetic interference (EMI), (4) radiation, (5) temperature, (6) relative humidity, (7) source of electrical supply, (8) sound levels, and (9) vibration. Other factors to consider in support of compliance with ISO/IEC 17025 are housekeeping practices, contamination control, and restricted access to work areas. This chapter discusses industry standards for environmental control and monitoring, housekeeping practices, effective contamination control, and subsidiary practices necessary for establishing good laboratory practices (GLP).

Summary of ISO/IEC 17025:2005 Requirement 5.3 (Accommodation and Environmental Conditions)

- Laboratories engaged in testing and calibration activities must maintain consistent sources of power, adequate lighting, and an appropriate environment to support the accuracy of testing and calibration performed. Ensuring that the operational environment does not adversely influence the accuracy of measurements should be considered a mission-critical activity. A laboratory's environmental conditions must be monitored and the actual conditions documented, as appropriate.

- Laboratories must monitor, control, and record environmental conditions. Additionally, laboratories must monitor and control (as applicable): biological sterility, particulate, the influence of EMI, radiation levels, relative humidity, consistency in laboratory electrical power, sound/noise, and levels of vibration to ensure that these environmental conditions do not negatively influence the results of testing and calibration.

- When functional areas within a laboratory are incompatible with the type of activities being performed, these areas must be segregated to prevent potential cross-contamination of results.

- Access to laboratory test areas shall be controlled as appropriate.

- Laboratories must use good housekeeping practices. When deemed necessary, special housekeeping procedures shall be established (janitorial services, cleaning of a controlled environment, etc.).

EFFECTIVE TOOLS FOR IMPLEMENTATION AND COMPLIANCE

To obtain accurate test and calibration results, laboratories must maintain adequate facilities, environmental controls, and good housekeeping. For example, temperature has a measurable effect on the accuracy of gage block calibration, so it is important that temperatures be controlled. The temperature associated with the dimensional calibration is typically 20°C ± 2.0°, so the laboratory would have to control and monitor the temperature for 20°C. The same would hold true for relative humidity if it were a factor influencing test or calibration accuracy.

Environmental Conditions

The laboratory must establish a procedure for environmental controls. At a minimum, the procedure should contain requirements for:

- Temperature (note: temperature ranges vary depending on how the area is used)

- Relative humidity

- Particulate count (for cleanroom environment)

- Positive pressure (required for cleanroom environment)

- Barometric pressure (if appropriate)

- Contamination control needed to meet sterility requirements (for cleanroom environment)

Also necessary to include in the procedure are: (1) control limits, (2) action limits, (3) methods for sample collection, (4) environmental monitoring, and (5) environmental testing (including equipment). For example, Magnehelic gages, needed to monitor the positive pressure of a cleanroom, must be included in the laboratory's calibration program.

Cleanroom/Controlled Environment

If the laboratory uses cleanroom environments for testing, the cleanroom must be properly validated. Using ISO 14644-1:1999 ("Cleanrooms and Associated Controlled

Environments") as a reference is highly recommended for the validation process. Many organizations specialize in generating and executing validation protocols for certifying a cleanroom. For further clarification of cleanroom classification, Table 1 of ISO 14644-1:1999 should be consulted. Retaining the validation protocols and reports and having copies available upon request for review by laboratory clients and regulatory bodies are important.

If the laboratory uses a controlled environment such as a cleanroom, a procedure for gowning is also required. The gowning procedure, depending on the cleanroom classification, may require a lab coat, full gown, hair cover, beard cover, booties, hand washing, makeup removal, and/or jewelry removal. Access to the controlled environment must also be controlled. Finally, the HEPA filtration system needed to support cleanroom operations must be included in the laboratory's preventive maintenance program.

Housekeeping

Good housekeeping is critical for maintaining the clean environment that is essential for accurate testing and calibration. An established procedure for housekeeping is vital and includes much more than emptying trash bins, sweeping the laboratory floors, and cleaning the restrooms. Workbenches, shelves, storage areas, desktops, chairs, benches, walls, and everything else within the laboratory must be kept clean and in good working order. Inside the cleanroom, housekeeping becomes even more challenging as contamination prevention and control are extremely important. Creating log sheets to document all cleaning activities is an important part of the housekeeping procedure. If a janitorial service is employed for housekeeping, the janitorial staff must be trained to the laboratory's housekeeping procedure and the training documented.

Facilities

The laboratory must have a facility that is adequate to support test and calibration operations. For example, the source of facility power is expected to be stable. If power interruptions are frequent, then a backup generator is a reasonable capital asset. Other facility requirements that need to be considered if they can potentially influence test and calibration accuracy include: (1) adequate lighting, (2) controlled access to restricted areas, (3) special shielding of laboratory areas from EMI, (4) radiation protection, or (5) use of lasers. It is important to maintain records of all facility maintenance activities, including the addition of facility-related equipment into the laboratory's preventive maintenance program, if appropriate (e.g., HEPA filtration system).

QUESTIONS TO CONSIDER DURING AN AUDIT

The questions in this section are not intended to be an all-inclusive list to be built into an internal or external audit checklist. However, they are relevant when evaluating the overall effectiveness of the laboratory's accommodation and environmental conditions.

1. Are the environmental conditions in the laboratory adequately controlled?

2. Does the laboratory have an established procedure for monitoring and controlling the laboratory environment?

3. What environmental elements are monitored?

4. Are records of environmental monitoring maintained?

5. Does the laboratory have an established procedure for housekeeping?

6. Does the laboratory employ a janitorial service for housekeeping? If so, are the employees of the service trained to the laboratory's housekeeping procedure?

CHAPTER REVIEW

The purpose of clause 5.3 is to ensure that laboratories consider the impact good facility management, environmental controls, and housekeeping have on the accuracy of test and calibration results. Laboratories must prepare adequate procedures for environmental controls, cleanrooms, and housekeeping. When appropriate, facility-related equipment that can influence the overall operational performance of the laboratory should be included in the laboratory's preventive maintenance program. It is an acceptable practice to outsource the validation of cleanrooms; however, copies of the protocols and validation reports must be retained and made available to clients and regulatory bodies. It is also an acceptable practice to outsource housekeeping as long as the janitorial service selected is trained to the laboratory's housekeeping procedure and the training is documented. Finally, all laboratory personnel are responsible for creating a work environment suitable for the performance of test and calibration work. Regardless of whether housekeeping is outsourced, all laboratory personnel must take responsibility for keeping their functional areas clean and orderly.

19

Test and Calibration Methods and Method Validation

Laboratories not only need to perform testing and calibration services in an appropriate environment, ISO/IEC 17025:2005 also requires substantial granularity with regard to the procedures used for testing and calibration. For example, established procedures are required to address: (1) sampling requirements, (2) handling, (3) transport, (4) storage, (5) preparation of items to be tested or calibrated, and (6) test methodologies. Measurement uncertainty and statistical techniques must also be considered as part of the analysis of test and calibration results. Another important tool related to the accuracy, reproducibility, and repeatability of measurement results is test method validation. Standard methods, laboratory-developed methods, and nonstandard methods used in the laboratory must be validated. The primary focus of the procedures and validated test methods is to obtain accurate measurement data using a stable measurement platform. As part of the discussion about compliance with clause 5.4, this chapter will explore measurement range, accuracy, measurement uncertainty, detection limit, linearity, repeatability, reproducibility, and industry-accepted practices for addressing measurement uncertainty and measurement error.

Summary of ISO/IEC 17025:2005 Requirement 5.4 (Test and Calibration Methods and Method Validation)

General

Laboratories must use appropriate methods and procedures when performing testing and calibration activities. Procedures should address sampling plans; the handling, transportation, and storage of test samples and equipment; and the preparation of test items and equipment for testing and calibration. Measurement uncertainty and statistical methodologies must also be considered. Laboratories must also develop and maintain adequate operational instructions for all equipment used for testing and calibration. When deviations from established laboratory testing and calibration methods occur, such deviations should be documented, written technical rationale provided, and the deviation approved by the customer.

Note: Recognized standards that contain sufficient granularity do not have to be rewritten by laboratories.

Selection of Methods

Laboratories must use test and calibration methods that are appropriate for the testing or calibration performed. These methods must support the needs of the customer. The expectation is that laboratories use the most recent version of recognized standards when possible. In cases where the customer does not specify a particular test or calibration method, the laboratory will select and employ a test or calibration method that is appropriate. Test methods developed or adopted by the laboratory must be appropriately validated prior to use. Prior to selecting a specific test method, laboratories must determine if they can effectively execute the method selected. If standard methods are employed by a laboratory and changes to a standard method occur, the laboratory must assess those changes and, if necessary, revalidate the standard prior to continued use. If a customer proposes a method that is out of date or inappropriate for the test or calibration to be performed, the laboratory must notify the customer of the issue.

Laboratory-Developed Methods

When laboratories develop and implement test and calibration methods for internal use, these activities must be adequately planned and executed by trained and qualified laboratory personnel. Plans must be documented and revised accordingly.

Nonstandard Methods

A laboratory may at some point need to employ a nonstandard method. Nonstandard methods require validation prior to their use. Additionally, customer approval is required. When nonstandard methods are used, they must align with customer specifications for testing and calibration.

Note: At a minimum, new test and calibration methods developed by laboratories should contain the following information: (1) method identification, (2) method scope, (3) description of the item to be tested or calibrated, (4) parameters and ranges of the test, (5) list of equipment to be used, (6) references to applicable standards or materials, (7) environmental conditions, (8) adequate description of the procedure to be executed, (9) pass/fail criteria, (10) data to be recorded (including methods of statistical analysis), and (11) the procedure for estimating measurement uncertainty.

Validation of Methods

- Definition of validation: Validation is the confirmation by examination and the provision of objective evidence that the particular requirements for a specific intended use are fulfilled.

- Laboratories must validate nonstandard methods and laboratory-developed methods. Validation activities shall be appropriate in depth and scale to ensure the accuracy and repeatability of each method for its intended use.

Note: Validations, when deemed necessary, can contain sampling procedures and procedures for handling and transportation.

Note: Techniques used to gauge method adequacy should contain: (1) calibration with a reference to a standard, (2) comparison of test and calibration results with other applicable methods, (3) interlaboratory comparisons, (4) assessment of influencers that may affect the test or calibration result obtained, and (5) assessment of measurement uncertainty.

Note: Laboratories must assess changes made to nonstandard methods and, when deemed necessary, execute a revalidation.

- Laboratories must assess the range and accuracy of values obtained when validated methods are used for testing and calibration. Measurement uncertainty, detection limit, measurement repeatability and reproducibility, and measurement robustness must be gauged and assessed.

Note: Validations must include: (1) specification of requirements, (2) determination of method characteristics, (3) verification that the targeted results can be achieved, and (4) a statement of method validity.

Note: During the development of methods, reviews of the development should be scheduled. All changes and modifications require review and approval.

Note: It is important to remember that method validation is a balancing act in which cost, risk, and technical possibilities must be considered.

Estimation of Uncertainty of Measurement

- Laboratories performing their own calibrations must establish a procedure that details the calibration process, including measurement uncertainty.

- Laboratories must establish, retain, and apply procedures to determine measurement uncertainty. The need to use measurement uncertainty tools is based on the robustness of the test method.

Note: The estimation of measurement uncertainty will be based in part on: (1) specific requirements of the test method employed, (2) customer-specific requirements, and (3) conformity assessments that are based on narrow limits.

Note: If a test method is well established and contains sufficient granularity with regard to the identification of sources of measurement uncertainty (including values), the application of the test method is deemed acceptable and in compliance with ISO/IEC 17025:2005.

- When laboratories estimate measurement uncertainty, all sources of uncertainty that can influence measurement accuracy must be included as part of the analytical process.

Note: Sources of measurement uncertainty that need to be considered are: (1) reference standards, (2) reference materials, (3) methods employed, (4) equipment employed, (5) environmental conditions, (6) operator variability, and (7) the operational properties and condition of items to be tested or calibrated.

Note: Reliability of the item being tested or calibrated is not a consideration with regard to measurement uncertainty.

Note: Further information expanding on the importance of measurement uncertainty can be found in the ISO 5725 series of standards.

Control of Data

- Data calculations and the transposition of data must be verified to ensure data accuracy is maintained.

- Laboratories that use an automated (computerized) approach to acquiring and processing data must ensure that:

  —The software employed is adequately documented and validated

  —Procedures are established for the purpose of protecting data

  —Equipment and computers used for data processing are properly maintained

  —The equipment is operated under appropriate environmental conditions

Note: Commercially procured software, provided such software is used as intended, does not require additional validation.

EFFECTIVE TOOLS FOR IMPLEMENTATION AND COMPLIANCE

Laboratories must use documented procedures and test methods for all test and calibration activities. The test methods employed must be validated, unless they are recognized standards developed by an organization such as ASTM International. Recognized standards should still be evaluated against their intended use within the laboratory. All other test methods should be validated for their intended use. Furthermore, written procedures and instructions should be generated to provide guidance for laboratory personnel who will perform the actual test and calibration work. Finally, controlled copies of published procedures and work instructions must be available at their point of use. If documentation is not available electronically, best practice is to create a document kiosk within each functional area of the laboratory to house relevant procedures and work instructions.

Selection of Test Methods

Whenever possible, recognized standards should be employed for testing and calibration. For calibration of electronic equipment such as oscilloscopes, voltmeters, and RLC bridges, the manufacturer's calibration method should be adequate. For a gage block set, other factors come into play, such as grade, which will require an appropriate reference standard to ensure calibration accuracy. The laboratory has the option of developing its own test method to support the mechanical/dimensional assessment and calibration of gage blocks. If the laboratory is tasked with testing the integrity of material or the assessment of biological products, then chances are good that the laboratory or the laboratory's client will have developed a test method (including sampling plan) for the products to be tested. Regardless of the test method selected for testing or calibration, the laboratory must document the approach and notify the customer of the method used.

Laboratory-Developed and Nonstandard Test Methods

Laboratories frequently develop their own test methods. The practice is perfectly acceptable; however, laboratory-developed test methods require the same stringent oversight as standard test methods, and thus validation is required. Laboratory-developed test methods must be validated for their intended use prior to releasing the test method for general laboratory use. Like laboratory-developed test methods, nonstandard test methods require validation prior to use.

Procedure Content

ISO/IEC 17025 requires that all new test or calibration procedures contain specific content. At a minimum, they should contain (as appropriate):

- Procedure identification

- Scope

- Description of test or calibration

- Test or calibration parameters

- List of necessary equipment to execute the test or calibration

- List of reference standards

- List of reference materials

- Detailed procedural steps

- Test or calibration acceptance or rejection criteria

- Data collection sheets and the data recording process

- Measurement uncertainty

- Process for documenting test or calibration deviations

Test Method Validation

Laboratories must validate all laboratory-developed methods, nonstandard test methods, and standard methods that have been modified for use, regardless of application. According to ISO 9001, validation is the confirmation, through objective evidence, that requirements for a specific intended use or application have been fulfilled. Similarly, according to 21 CFR Part 820 (the FDA's Quality System Regulation), validation comprises documented evidence that provides a high degree of assurance that a specific process will consistently produce a product that meets its predetermined specifications and quality attributes.

Although not specifically required by ISO/IEC 17025, best practice is for a laboratory to write a stand-alone procedure for validation. There are also specific attributes and data quality objectives ISO/IEC 17025 requires to support validation, including:

- Accuracy
- Precision
- Specificity
- Detection limit
- Limit of quantitation
- Linearity
- Range
- Ruggedness
- Robustness

If all the data quality objectives are achieved based on review and analysis of the data, then the test method is considered to be validated according to ISO/IEC 17025.

The National Association of Testing Authorities (NATA) in Australia developed a list of questions that can be used to frame the scope of the method requiring validation. The following questions are from NATA's Technical Note 17:

- What is the purpose of measurement (what is to be identified and why)?

- What are the likely sample matrices?

- Are interferences expected, and if so, should they be determined?

- What is the scope (what are the expected concentration levels or ranges)?

- Are there any specific legislative or regulatory requirements?

- Are there any specific equipment accommodation and environmental conditions that need to be considered?

- What type of equipment is to be used?

- Is the method for one specific instrument, or should it be used with all instruments of the same type?

- What is the method used for the preparation, sub-sampling, procedure, and equipment?

Measurement Uncertainty

To understand the concept of measurement uncertainty, the measurement process must first be understood. A measurement comprises a series of operations executed to calculate or determine a value. The measurement process essentially transforms inputs into outputs. Regardless of how well defined a measurement process is, obtaining identical repeat observations is almost impossible. This is due to the introduction of variability into the measurement process. Variables introduced into the measurement process, such as laboratory environmental conditions, test methods, different technicians, and materials and equipment employed, result in measurement uncertainty and must be accounted for as part of the measurement process (Type-B estimates of uncertainty). Statistically, estimating uncertainty can be broken down into two categories: Type-A estimates (estimates obtained from sample data) and Type-B estimates (uncertainty estimates for measurement process errors resulting from reference attribute bias, display resolution, operator bias, and computation and environmental factors), also known as heuristic estimates.

For laboratories, procedures must be written and applied to estimate measurement uncertainty for all calibrations. Measurement uncertainty values must be stated in the calibration certificates and test reports.

Control of Data

Data accuracy is a fundamental requirement for a laboratory. Laboratories should implement a system for verifying the accuracy of the data collected. If the data collection process is automated or uses a computer, the software needs to be validated. The equipment employed in support of an automated data collection system (including computers) needs to be placed in an appropriate environment and maintained to preserve functional capabilities. The laboratory must establish a procedure that clearly defines its entire data collection process. In accordance with ISO/IEC 17025, the procedure generated for control of data must include:

- Data protection
- Data integrity and confidentiality associated with data collection and data entry
- Data storage and backup
- Data retrieval

- Data processing
- Data accessibility
- Data transmission

QUESTIONS TO CONSIDER DURING AN AUDIT

The questions in this section are not intended to be an all-inclusive list to be built into an internal or external audit checklist. However, they are relevant when evaluating the overall effectiveness of a laboratory's test, calibration, and validation methods.

1. Are the laboratory's test and calibration methods documented by written procedures and/or work instructions?

2. Does the laboratory have an established procedure for test method validation?

3. Are work instructions and procedures available at their point of use?

4. Have laboratory-designed test and calibration methods been properly validated?

5. Does the laboratory employ nonstandard test and calibration methods for testing and calibration?

6. Are nonstandard methods validated prior to their use?

7. Are range, accuracy, measurement uncertainty, detection limits, measurement linearity, reproducibility, and repeatability considered when validating test methods?

8. How does the laboratory evaluate measurement uncertainty?

9. Does the laboratory have an established procedure for addressing measurement uncertainty?

10. Does the laboratory perform a cursory review of obtained data for accuracy?

11. Does the laboratory use computer software for testing and calibration?

12. Has the computer software been properly validated?

13. Does the laboratory have an established procedure for the handling, storage, transportation, and preventive maintenance of equipment?

CHAPTER REVIEW

Because the application of standard, laboratory-developed, and nonstandard test methods form the foundation of testing and calibration work, test methods must be validated for their intended use. Standard test methods developed by a recognized body such as ASTM do not require formal validation, provided the methods are used as intended. All other test methods must be validated by the laboratory. Identifying factors of measurement uncertainty is also important in obtaining accurate test and calibration results. In fact, measurement uncertainty is such an important influencer that ISO/IEC 17025 requires laboratories to establish a procedure to address it. Finally, maintaining data accuracy and integrity is also a fundamental requirement for laboratories. Once again, control of data is so important that ISO/IEC 17025 requires laboratories to establish a procedure.

20

Equipment

ISO/IEC 17025:2005 requires laboratories to be properly equipped for testing and calibration activities. The laboratory's equipment and software must be capable of obtaining accurate measurements when used in a testing and calibration environment. Additionally, laboratory equipment must always be calibrated to a defined specification and/or standard prior to its use. If a laboratory needs to lease a piece of equipment for a specific purpose, the leased equipment must meet all laboratory requirements and the requirements of the ISO standard. Laboratories must also maintain records for their equipment. ISO/IEC 17025:2005 describes specific requirements for record keeping that laboratories must comply with. Because of its overall impact on the performance of a laboratory, record keeping will be discussed in detail in this chapter. Furthermore, ISO/IEC 17025 incorporates requirements that are similar to ISO 9001:2008 clause 7.6, "Control of Monitoring and Measuring Devices." For example, using calibration stickers to reflect calibration status and safeguarding equipment from adjustments are prominent requirements of ISO/IEC 17025 clause 5.5. Finally, the proper handling of equipment is necessary to ensure the accuracy of the measurement results obtained. When evidence indicates that equipment has been mishandled or failed to perform within its stated specifications, the laboratory must pursue appropriate action, including immediate removal of suspect equipment from service. This chapter will provide practical guidance for complying with clause 5.5.

Summary of ISO/IEC 17025:2005 Requirement 5.5 (Equipment)

- The laboratory must have in place all essential equipment for sampling, measurement, and testing.

- The equipment and its supporting software must be capable of providing the required measurement accuracy for testing and calibration.

- Only trained and authorized personnel should be allowed to operate equipment. The manufacturer's operating instructions must be made available for use.

- All equipment and its supporting service must be properly identified with a unique number or serial number.

- Laboratories must maintain records of their equipment and its supporting software. Records should contain:

  —Equipment identity

  —Manufacturer's name, equipment name, and serial number

  —Evidence that the equipment functions within operating parameters

  —Location in the lab (e.g., equipment owner)

  —Manufacturer's instructions (e.g., manual)

  —Calibration date(s)

  —Calibration certificate(s)

  —Preventive maintenance records (as applicable)

  —Records of repairs

  —All other records relevant to the piece of equipment

- Laboratories must have a written procedure that delineates:

—Proper handling of equipment

—Proper storage of equipment

—Proper transportation of equipment

—Proper use of equipment

—Proper preventive maintenance

Note: If equipment is used outside of the laboratory environment, a written procedure must be generated to define the process.

- Nonconforming equipment should be removed from service and the nonconforming event investigated. Corrective action should be pursued as appropriate.

- Equipment requiring calibration must be clearly labeled with a calibration sticker that reflects the proper calibration status, including the date calibration is due.

- If equipment is removed from the laboratory (direct control), the equipment must be evaluated prior to returning to use within the laboratory.

- When performance checks of equipment are required to maintain calibration consistency, a written procedure must identify the performance confirmation process.

- When correction factors are required to support calibration, the laboratory must document the use of these factors in a procedure.

- Equipment employed for testing and calibration must be safeguarded from adjustments that would invalidate the results of testing and calibration.

EFFECTIVE TOOLS FOR IMPLEMENTATION AND COMPLIANCE

Laboratories should be fully equipped with the appropriate tools and equipment needed to collect samples and execute testing and calibration. The equipment and software (as applicable) must be capable of obtaining accurate and repeatable test and calibration results. Equipment range, accuracy, resolution, and measurement uncertainty are factors that laboratories need to consider when selecting laboratory equipment. All laboratory equipment must be calibrated prior to use, if applicable. In fact, an effective calibration and preventive maintenance program in the laboratory is extremely important and should include a requirement for measurement traceability of calibrated equipment that is aligned to the NIST standard or to the equivalent standard outside of the United States (see Figure 20.1).

Training and Operation

Training is extremely important when it comes to operating testing and calibration equipment. Each engineer, operator, and technician must be properly trained in the use of laboratory equipment. In some cases, the equipment manufacturer may have to provide the training because of equipment complexity. Regardless, the training should be documented in personnel training files. Best practice is to include the requirement to operate specific pieces of equipment in the laboratory's job descriptions. Furthermore, making the operation manual for each piece of equipment available at its point of use is highly recommended. A good practice is to build a kiosk in the laboratory that houses all relevant work instructions, procedures, and manuals.

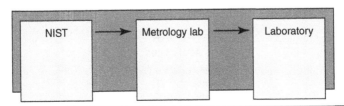

Figure 20.1   Traceability block diagram.

Equipment Identification and Record Keeping

All equipment employed for testing and calibration should be properly identified. A best practice and a requirement of ISO 9001 is to affix a label to each piece of equipment that includes: (1) the equipment identification number, (2) the calibration date, and (3) the calibration due date (see Figure 20.2). For standards sent to a metrology lab for calibration, this is already an accepted practice.

When writing the procedure for calibration and preventive maintenance, ISO/IEC 17025 requires specific pieces of information to be collected and retained in each equipment file. At a minimum, the following information must be included in each piece of equipment's master file:

- The identification of equipment (including software if applicable)

- The name of the manufacturer

- The equipment's serial number

- Verification and validation activities, including functional performance

- Equipment owner/location

- Manufacturer's operating instructions/manual or a pointer to the location of the manual (e.g., kiosk)

- Calibration records (reports, certificates, adjustments, acceptance criteria, and calibration due date)

```
             ACME Labs
     Equipment ID#: ATL-0001
     Cal date: 11/21/12
     Cal due: 11/20/13
```

Figure 20.2   Sample label.

- Preventive maintenance schedule (if applicable)
- History of equipment problems (damage, out-of-tolerance reports, malfunctions, modifications, and repairs)

Handling and Storage

The laboratory's procedure for calibration and preventive maintenance must address the handling, storage, and transportation of laboratory equipment. When not in use and when practical, laboratory equipment should be adequately protected in a suitable environment. Whenever possible, best practice is to store and transport laboratory equipment in its original carrying case. When equipment is in place on the laboratory floor, it is important to place it where it cannot be dropped accidentally or damaged.

Nonconforming Equipment

When equipment has been mishandled, provides erroneous results, or functions outside of its specification limits, it must be taken out of service immediately. The first thing that the laboratory should do is tag the piece of suspect equipment with an NCR tag (see Figure 9.1). The nonconformance should be handled in accordance with the guidance provided in Chapter 9, including the opening of the NCR.

Additional Influencers

If laboratory equipment is moved outside of the laboratory's direct control, its functional performance and calibration status must be verified prior to its return to service. In a perfect world, metrology facilities would never make mistakes and equipment would never be damaged during routine transportation; however, the world is far from perfect. Upon receipt, the equipment should be checked to verify that a new calibration sticker has been affixed, the equipment is functional (it turns on), and the calibration certificate is accurate. Calibration results should routinely be compared with previous results to ensure equipment performance remains consistent. If the metrology lab determines the equipment to be out of tolerance, an adjustment to the calibration interval is in order.

In some cases, correction factors may be associated with equipment or software. Again, requirements should be documented in the calibration procedure. Correction factors should reside in the equipment file and be updated as required.

Dedicating some pieces of laboratory equipment to a specific test or calibration is not unusual, particularly when the test or calibration setup is time consuming. Most equipment has the capability to lock potentiometers into place to prevent measurement adjustments. In these cases, locking adjustments into place through the use of lock-out tape or the application of an epoxy adhesive is often beneficial. If software is loaded onto laboratory equipment prior to its use, the software must be controlled. Only the most current version of software/firmware should be available at its point of use.

QUESTIONS TO CONSIDER DURING AN AUDIT

The questions in this section are not intended to be an all-inclusive list to be built into an internal or external audit checklist. However, they are relevant when evaluating the overall effectiveness of a laboratory's equipment.

1. Does the laboratory have adequate measurement equipment to support testing and calibration?

2. Is equipment and supporting software capable of supporting the accuracy needed for testing and calibration?

3. Are instructions for the proper operation of equipment available?

4. Is equipment being operated by trained operators?

5. Are training records available for the operators and are the records current?

6. Are records being maintained for each piece of equipment?

7. What type of information do the equipment records contain?

8. Does the laboratory have an established procedure for addressing nonconforming equipment?

9. Does the laboratory permit use of its equipment outside of the laboratory environment?

10. How is equipment used outside the laboratory identified?

11. Is equipment used outside the laboratory environment evaluated prior to its return to use inside the laboratory?

12. Is the laboratory employing correction factors to support calibration?

13. Is test equipment being safeguarded from unauthorized adjustments that could influence measurement accuracy?

CHAPTER REVIEW

Laboratories must select and employ equipment that can provide accurate and repeatable measurements. As part of the selection process, equipment range, accuracy, resolution, and measurement uncertainty must be considered. Laboratory personnel must be properly trained and the training documented before they are allowed to operate equipment. Equipment must be properly identified, including the calibration status. To maintain equipment that can obtain accurate and repeatable measurement, the laboratory must write a calibration procedure with sufficient granularity that defines the laboratory's equipment calibration and preventive maintenance program. When nonconforming equipment is identified, it must be removed from service and the nonconformance processed in accordance with clause 4.9 of ISO/IEC 17025 (see Chapter 9).

21

Measurement Traceability

The accuracy of measurements obtained during testing or calibration can be directly attributed to the measuring equipment used. The cornerstone of measurement traceability is calibration. As discussed in Chapter 20, all monitoring and measuring equipment must be properly calibrated. ISO/IEC 17025:2005 specifically requires laboratories to establish a program and procedure for calibration. Another requirement of the calibration process is maintaining traceability to a recognized standard. The fundamental question to ask when using primary measurement standards, national standards, and international standards associated with calibration should be: When is each standard appropriate for use? Another challenge for laboratories is the traceability of calibrations and measurements to the International System of Units (SI units, from *système international d'unités*), through the use of a national standard. In some cases, the use of SI units is just not practical. The calibration, use, and management of reference standards is also a requirement of ISO/IEC 17025 that needs an established procedure. This chapter presents a proactive approach for ensuring laboratories achieve and sustain compliance with clause 5.6, including different approaches to managing calibration and reference standards.

Summary of ISO/IEC 17025:2005 Requirement 5.6 (Measurement Traceability)

General

- Laboratories must establish a procedure that delineates their entire equipment calibration program.

Note: The calibration program must be based on a systematic approach to all calibration activities.

Calibration

- For calibration laboratories, calibrations and measurements must be traceable to a recognized standard (e.g., the International System of Units).

- Calibration laboratories may establish traceability to their own measurement standards, provided the measurement standards are traceable to a national standard (e.g., NIST).

Note: Calibration laboratories that meet the accreditation requirements of ISO/IEC 17025:2005 should be deemed assured.

Note: Traceability can be achieved through reference to a primary standard.

Note: Laboratories that maintain their own primary standards can claim traceability if these standards are compared with and traceable to a national standard.

Note: Calibration certificates must clearly reflect the specification used for measurement comparisons.

Note: When national or international standards are referenced for traceability, it should be assumed that these standards meet the intent of SI units.

Note: Traceability to a national standard does not require the use of the national metrology laboratory (regardless of the national standard used).

Note: Laboratories that need to obtain traceability from a national metrology institute other than their own may do so.

Note: Employing multiple steps to demonstrate the unbroken chain of calibration is acceptable.

- Not all calibrations can be performed and expressed in SI units. When it is not possible, traceability to an appropriate standard is acceptable. ISO/IEC 17025:2005 permits:

    —The employment of certified reference materials

    —The employment of consensus standards

Testing

- Testing laboratories must establish a procedure that delineates their entire equipment calibration program.

Note: When calibration influences measurement uncertainty, strict adherence to the calibration program is critical.

- When traceability to SI units is not possible, using certified reference materials and consensus standards is acceptable.

Reference Standards

- Laboratories must calibrate their reference standards.

Intermediate Checks

- When deemed appropriate for ensuring the accuracy of standards (primary, reference, working, or transfer), performance checks of equipment should be performed.

Transport and Storage

- Laboratories must establish written procedures that delineate the proper handling of reference standards and reference materials.

Note: If reference standards are used outside of the laboratory environment, a written procedure shall be generated to define the process.

EFFECTIVE TOOLS FOR IMPLEMENTATION AND COMPLIANCE

Laboratories must calibrate their equipment prior to use. As stated in Chapter 20, laboratories must establish a calibration program that is documented by a written procedure. Besides calibration, the program created by the laboratory must also include the laboratory's processes for:

- Checking equipment

- Controlling measurement standards

- Maintaining measurement standards

- Using reference materials as measurement standards

SI Units

For laboratories that execute calibration work, the equipment must be capable of obtaining accurate measurement and calibration results, while also being traceable to the International System of Units. SI units, which are based on the metric system, have been adopted by most countries. However, the United States has not adopted the SI unit system. Figure 21.1 depicts the seven baseline SI units and the relationships among them.

Calibration and Traceability

According to ISO 19011, calibration is the set of operations that establish, under specified conditions, the relationship among values indicated by a measuring instrument, a measuring system or values represented by a material measure, and the corresponding known values of a measurand (the quantity to be measured). Traceability is also a critical component of the calibration process.

According to a working paper developed by the United Nations Industrial Development Organization (UNIDO 2009),

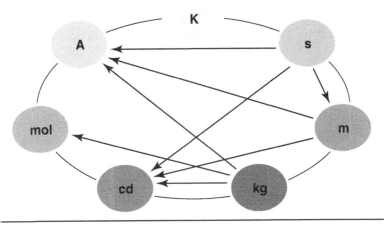

Figure 21.1   The seven baseline SI units.

traceability refers to validating calibration of a measuring standard or instrument by step-by-step comparison with accepted national or international standards.

Together, calibration and traceability define a laboratory's calibration program. Basically, all equipment employed in the calibration process must eventually be traceable back to a national standard such as NIST, through the use of primary and secondary (reference) standards. When a laboratory employs a metrology laboratory to calibrate equipment, the metrology laboratory selected should be accredited to ISO/IEC 17025. Compliance with ISO/IEC 17025, although not a complete guarantee, reflects an organization's capacity to demonstrate technical competence, measurement capability, and measurement traceability.

Use of Independent Metrology Laboratories

As previously stated, when employing an independent metrology laboratory, the laboratory selected must be accredited to ISO/IEC 17025. Prior to its addition to the ASL, the laboratory should be evaluated by using the tools mentioned in Chapters 5 and 6. The metrology laboratory should provide actual values associated with each calibration, as part of the certificate of calibration.

Calibration Procedure Content

Besides the mandatory content requirements specified in Chapter 20, best practice is to incorporate the requirements described in clause 7.6 of ISO 9001 ("Control of Monitoring and Measuring Equipment") into the laboratory's calibration procedure. At a minimum, the following requirements must be addressed in the procedure:

- Laboratory equipment must be calibrated at predefined intervals against standards that are traceable to a national standard, e.g., NIST. The calibration intervals must be included in the procedure.

- Laboratory equipment (if applicable) must be able to be adjusted or readjusted, as necessary.

- The calibration status of laboratory equipment must be properly identified (see Figure 20.2).

- Laboratory equipment must be safeguarded against adjustments that would invalidate the results of obtained measurements.

- Laboratory equipment must be protected from damage and deterioration during handling, maintenance, and storage.

- Laboratories must perform a comparative analysis of calibration data against calibration data obtained previously. This is why having metrology labs provide the actual calibration data is so important.

- Laboratories must act in accordance with clause 4.9 of ISO/IEC 17025 ("Control of Nonconforming Testing and/or Calibration Work") when nonconforming equipment has been identified.

- Laboratories must maintain records of all calibration activities. Calibration records should be managed in accordance with clause 4.13 ("Control of Records").

Testing

Testing within the laboratory requires the use of calibrated measuring equipment and requires traceability. When equipment is employed for testing, it must support the need to address measurement uncertainty. Additionally, testing must be performed within an adequate laboratory environment. For example, if the testing is being performed on biologics, then the expectation is that the laboratory will perform these tests in a controlled environment (cleanroom).

Calibration of Reference Standards

Laboratories must establish procedures for all their reference standards. Reference standards should be considered restricted-use standards because they should only be used for calibration. The metrology lab tasked with the calibration of reference standards must ensure the calibration is performed with equipment traceable directly to a national standard (e.g., NIST).

Traceability of Reference Materials

As part of the calibration procedure, the laboratory must define the requirements for the control of reference materials. Whenever possible, reference materials should be traceable to SI units (except in the United States). Using certified reference materials is always a best practice; however, if certification is not possible, the laboratory must establish a procedure for validating reference materials.

QUESTIONS TO CONSIDER DURING AN AUDIT

The questions in this section are not intended to be an all-inclusive list to be built into an internal or external audit check-list. However, they are relevant when evaluating the overall effectiveness of a laboratory's measurement traceability.

1. Is all laboratory measurement equipment used for testing and calibration calibrated?

2. Does the laboratory have an established procedure documenting its calibration program?

3. Are measurements traceable to SI units?

4. If the laboratory does not use traceability to SI units, has traceability to an appropriate measurement standard been established?

5. Does the laboratory use reference materials to support calibration?

6. Does the laboratory have an established procedure for the calibration of reference standards?

7. Does the laboratory have an established procedure for the handling, transportation, and storage of reference materials and standards?

CHAPTER REVIEW

Laboratories must establish a calibration program documented by an established procedure. All testing and calibration performed within the laboratory must be performed with calibrated equipment and traceability to a national standard (e.g., NIST) to ensure measurements obtained are accurate and repeatable. Metrology facilities selected for equipment calibration (e.g., reference standards) should be ISO/IEC 17025 accredited. Calibrated reference standards should be reserved for performing calibrations only. Using certified reference materials is always a best practice; however, if certification is not possible, validating the use of reference material is the next best thing.

22

Sampling

Laboratories must establish and implement procedures for the purpose of sampling materials, substances, and products being tested. The sampling plans must be based on recognized statistical methodologies, and such plans must be made available at the point of use. The sampling plan procedure must delineate: (1) sample selection, (2) sampling plan, (3) sample withdraw, and (4) sample preparation. To comply with clause 5.7 of ISO/IEC 17025:2005, directly correlating sampling plans with a recognized sampling standard such as ANSI/ASQ Z1.4 is considered best practice. It is essential that the approach to sampling does not influence the accuracy and validity of test and calibration results. In support of the sampling requirement, laboratories must also establish a procedure to record data collected during testing and calibration activities.

Summary of ISO/IEC 17025:2005
Requirement 5.7 (Sampling)

- Laboratories must establish procedures covering the use of sampling plans and ensure such procedures are available where testing and calibration is performed (point of use). Sampling plans must be based on valid statistical methodologies. The approach to sampling delineated within a procedure must identify and address variables that must be controlled to ensure testing and calibration results remain valid.

Note: ISO/IEC 17025:2005 defines sampling as "a defined procedure whereby a part of a substance, material, or product is taken to provide for testing or calibration of a representative sample of the whole."

Note: Laboratories must delineate the sample selection process in their sampling plan procedures.

- Customer requests to deviate from the laboratory's established procedure for sampling must be documented. These deviations must be communicated to all affected laboratory personnel.

- Laboratories must establish procedures to record data collected during sampling for testing and calibration. Examples of information to consider and record are environmental conditions, functional diagrams, pictures, drawings, numbering schemes, or similar means to identify sample location. If deemed appropriate, the statistical means and relevancy of the sampling plan should also be documented.

EFFECTIVE TOOLS FOR IMPLEMENTATION AND COMPLIANCE

Laboratories must have and use sampling plans and establish procedures that govern sampling plans, delineate custom sampling plans, or both. According to NIST/SEMATECH:

A sampling plan is a detailed outline of which measurements will be taken at what times, on which material, in what manner, and by whom. Sampling plans should be designed in such a way that the resulting data will contain a representative sample of the parameters of interest and allow for all questions, as stated in the goals, to be answered. (NIST/SEMATECH 2012)

Sampling Plans

Depending on the type of test or calibration work being performed in the laboratory, established sampling plans such as those authored by the American National Standards Institute (ANSI) and the American Society for Quality (ASQ) may be practical. Attribute acceptance plans such as ANSI/ASQ Z1.4-2008; zero acceptance number sampling plans (Table 22.1); and variable acceptance plans, such as ANSI/ASQ Z1.9-2008, have proven to be effective in a laboratory environment.

Development of a Sampling Plan

When laboratories develop their own sampling plans, eight elements must be considered in order for the sampling plan to be statistically relevant and effective:

1. The sampling plan must contain purpose and scope statements

2. The sampling plan should contain references (as appropriate)

3. The sampling plan should include a section for roles and responsibilities

4. The sampling plan must cover: (a) the parameters selected for measurement, (b) the range of the values to be measured, and (c) the accuracy and resolution required to obtain these measurements

5. The process for how and when samples will be obtained must be specified

6. Actual sample sizes need to be specified within the plan

7. The sampling plan must contain requirements for data collection, data recording, and storage

8. The sampling plan must be verified prior to its release for use in the laboratory

Table 22.1 Zero acceptance number sampling plan (c = 0).

Lot size	.010	.015	.025	.040	.065	.10	.15	.25	.40	.65	1.0	1.5	2.5	4.0	6.5
2–8	All	All	All	All	All	All	All	All	All	All	All	All	5	3	3
9–15	All	All	All	All	All	All	All	All	All	All	13	8	5	3	3
16–25	All	All	All	All	All	All	All	All	32	20	13	8	5	3	3
26–50	All	All	All	All	All	All	All	All	32	20	13	8	7	7	5
51–90	All	All	All	All	All	All	80	50	32	20	13	11	11	8	5
91–150	All	All	All	All	All	125	80	50	32	20	13	13	11	9	6
151–280	All	All	All	All	200	125	80	50	48	29	29	19	13	10	7
281–500	All	All	All	315	200	125	80	75	73	47	29	21	16	11	9
501–1200	All	800	500	315	200	125	80	75	73	47	34	27	19	15	11
1201–3200	1250	800	500	315	200	192	120	116	73	53	42	35	23	18	13
3201–10,000	1250	800	500	315	200	192	189	116	86	68	50	38	29	22	15
10,001–35,000	1250	800	500	315	300	294	189	135	108	77	60	46	35	29	15
35,001–150,000	1250	800	500	490	476	294	218	170	123	96	74	56	40	29	15
150,001–500,000	1250	800	750	715	476	345	270	200	156	119	90	64	40	29	15
500,001 and over	1250	1200	1112	715	556	435	303	244	189	143	102	64	40	29	15

Sampling Plan Deviations

If a customer asks a laboratory to deviate from established sampling plans, the deviation should always be documented. In some cases, a laboratory's customer may have its own sampling plans. These sampling plans should always be reviewed as part of the initial request for quotation from the customer and be built into the laboratory's testing and/or calibration documentation for the customer. When stating the results of testing or calibration work, the sampling data must be included in the test reports or within the calibration certificate.

Recording of Data

The development of a sampling plan requires the inclusion of the data recording process. ISO/IEC 17025 specifically requires these elements:

- Identification of the sampling plan used

- The environmental conditions if relevant to the process

- The accurate identification of the location(s) of the samples taken

- The statistical plan the sampling plan is based on (if appropriate)

QUESTIONS TO CONSIDER DURING AN AUDIT

The questions in this section are not intended to be an all-inclusive list to be built into an internal or external audit checklist. However, they are relevant when evaluating the overall effectiveness of a laboratory's sampling methodologies.

1. Does the laboratory have an established procedure for the use of sampling plans?

2. Are sampling plans available at their point of use to support testing and calibration?

3. Are deviations from the sampling plans documented?

4. Are sampling plans verified prior to their release?

5. Are the sampling plans statistically relevant?

CHAPTER REVIEW

Laboratories must establish procedures for sampling plan creation and sampling plan utilization. The sampling plans engineered by laboratories must be verified prior to their release for use. Regardless of the sampling approach, the sampling plans employed must be statistically relevant. ANSI/ASQ has well established sampling plans that can be used in the laboratory environment, if practical. If a customer requires a laboratory to deviate from its documented procedures or if a customer has its own sampling plan procedure, this deviation must be documented in the test report or calibration certificate. Finally, ISO/IEC 17025 has some specific requirements for the data recording process.

23

Handling of Test and Calibration Items

Like ISO 9001:2008, ISO/IEC 17025:2005 requires laboratories to establish procedures that delineate: (1) transportation, (2) receipt, (3) handling, (4) protection, (5) storage, (6) retention, and (7) disposal of test and calibration items as applicable. Similar laboratory procedures are required to prevent damage, deterioration, or loss of test and calibration items during storage, handling, and preparation. The goal for laboratories should be the protection of the integrity of the test item or the equipment submitted for calibration. Laboratories are also required to implement a process for identification and traceability of test and calibration items. Finally, laboratories must be able to reasonably assess items submitted for testing and calibration and ascertain the suitability of the items prior to the commencement of testing or calibration work.

Summary of ISO/IEC 17025:2005 Requirement 5.8 (Handling of Test and Calibration Items)

- Laboratories must establish a procedure or a set of procedures that delineates how the laboratory handles items received for test and calibration and ultimately returns them to the customer. At a minimum, the procedure(s) must address transportation, receipt, handling, storage, retention, and disposal processes.

- Laboratories must create and implement an effective system to identify and maintain traceability of items tested and calibrated in the laboratory. The system must support effective data retention and traceability for the life of the items tested and calibrated.

- When laboratories receive items for testing or calibration and the initial assessment of these items reflects a nonconformance or insufficient granularity regarding the test or calibration method, laboratories must contact the customer for further instructions.

- Laboratories must establish procedures and operate within an appropriate environment/facility to prevent damage, deterioration, or loss of test or calibration items. Additionally, when a controlled environment is required to perform testing and calibration, the environmental conditions must be monitored and controlled. Furthermore, laboratories must provide adequate storage and security when such methods are required.

Note: When testing is complete and items are returned to service, laboratories must take care to avoid damage to such items.

Note: A sampling procedure, including procedures relating to storage and transportation of samples, should be provided to personnel responsible for transporting samples.

Note: Reasons for keeping test and calibration items secure can vary greatly.

EFFECTIVE TOOLS FOR IMPLEMENTATION AND COMPLIANCE

Laboratories must establish procedures for the transportation, receipt, handling, protection, storage, retention, and disposal of test and calibration items. These elements can be included in different laboratory procedures, or the laboratory can choose to write a stand-alone procedure for them. As long as the requirements are documented in a procedure and the laboratory complies with that procedure, then the laboratory can claim compliance with clause 5.8 of ISO/IEC 17025.

Designated Areas and Transportation

As part of the procedure, the laboratory should list the designated areas within the lab affected by the procedure. For example, the receipt and transportation of items will occur in one of two ways: (1) laboratory personnel will collect the items at a customer site and transport them back to the laboratory in a laboratory vehicle, or (2) items will be shipped to the laboratory through a commercial shipping carrier such as UPS. In any event the entry point into the laboratory will be the receiving dock. If the laboratory routinely picks up and delivers test and calibration items, then the transportation of these items needs to be documented in the procedure. It is also a best practice to document all shipping modalities, including packaging, in an established procedure.

Receipt and Identification of Test and Calibration Items

Upon receipt of the items, the laboratory should perform an initial assessment for damage related to handling and transportation. If the item has been damaged during transportation, the event should be documented and the customer contacted for further instructions. Laboratories should have a holding area for damaged items. If the received item is acceptable, the receipt should be logged into the laboratory's receiving log. The receiving log can be electronic (Figure 23.1), similar to logs used in a material requirements planning (MRP) system. Receiving personnel must be properly trained and capable of documenting the as-received condition of test and calibration items. As part of the receiving process, the laboratory will: (1) assign a unique work order number (employed for identification and traceability) to the item, (2) affix a tag or label to the item showing the work order number, and (3) print the work order that describes all of the processing steps. For electronic MRP systems, the work order may simply be a compilation of sequential steps that contains a brief description of the work to be performed and a barcode.

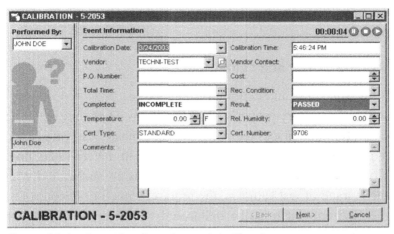

Figure 23.1 Example of an electronic calibration system menu.

Received Test and/or Calibration Item Inspection

Depending on the type of test or calibration item, an inspection that is more thorough than the typical identification and damage assessment upon receipt may be required. All additional inspection and assessment activities performed on items as part of inspection must be documented. In many cases, the inspection information can be recorded on the work order. As with the receiving process, if a test or calibration item is found unfit for testing or calibration, the item should be placed on hold and the customer notified. Because the test or calibration item has now entered the laboratory's work stream, the nonconformance should be documented in accordance with clause 4.9 of ISO/IEC 17025.

Handling and Protection of Test and Calibration Items

Laboratories must properly handle items to protect them from damage and deterioration while in their custody. For test items, the best practice is to place them into protective carrying totes if possible. For equipment sent to the laboratory for calibration, the best practice is to use the manufacturer's carrying case for each piece of equipment. Using adequate protection schemes is never optional.

Storage of Test and Calibration Items

Sometimes test and calibration items must be stored. Assuming the laboratory properly identifies items when they enter the laboratory and places them in protective bins or carrying cases, storage is nothing more than an exercise in material handling. However, if environmental considerations are associated with the storage of test samples, the requirements for the control of the environment must be delineated within a procedure. For example, if items to be stored require temperature and relative humidity control, these parameters must be defined in a procedure and evidence of the suitability of the environment collected. Additionally, test and calibration items should be stored in a manner that facilitates their easy retrieval. Furthermore, security should always be a concern for laboratories. Storage areas should be considered restricted access areas, with access limited to laboratory personnel who have functional responsibility for item storage.

Retention and Disposal of Test and Calibration Items

Retention and disposal pertains to test samples (equipment sent to a laboratory for calibration will ultimately be returned to its owner, the customer). Some customers want the samples returned with the test report, and some customers ask the laboratory to retain the samples. Because ISO/IEC 17025 provides no predefined retention times, the laboratory must determine retention time for the samples. If the test samples do not degrade over time, then best practice is to retain the sample for the same duration as the test report. If samples do degrade over time, then 90 days is a reasonable duration to retain samples prior to their disposal. However, regardless of the approach to sample retention and disposal, the time frames must clearly be delineated within a procedure and the retention periods clearly conveyed to the customer.

QUESTIONS TO CONSIDER DURING AN AUDIT

The questions in this section are not intended to be an all-inclusive list to be built into an internal or external audit checklist. However, they are relevant when evaluating the overall effectiveness of laboratory handling of test and calibration items.

1. Does the laboratory have an established procedure for the handling, receipt, transportation, protection, storage, retention, and, if applicable, disposal of test and calibration items?

2. How does the laboratory identify test and calibration items?

3. Are items received by the laboratory evaluated upon receipt for damage and operational performance anomalies?

4. Are laboratory customers promptly notified when items are received in a damaged, nonoperational, or degraded condition?

5. Does the laboratory have the appropriate facilities to avoid deterioration, loss, or damage to the test or calibration items during storage, handling, and preparation?

6. Does the laboratory have an established procedure for handling items that must be secured?

CHAPTER REVIEW

Laboratories must establish procedures for the transportation, receipt, handling, protection, storage, retention, and disposal of test and calibration items. When test and calibration items are received by a laboratory, an initial damage assessment must occur. This initial assessment must be documented. Best practice is to place test items into protective totes or bins. Equipment sent to a laboratory for calibration and repair work should be placed in its original carrying case to prevent damage. Laboratories must provide adequate storage conditions to protect and preserve test and calibration items. Retention and disposal time periods must be defined in a procedure. The customer should be aware of the laboratory's test item disposal policy. If special environmental controls are necessary, the requirements for environmental controls must be documented in a procedure and the storage area monitored for compliance.

24

Assuring the Quality of Test and Calibration Results

Because obtaining and reporting test and calibration results that are accurate is the primary goal of testing and calibration laboratories, assuring the quality of the results is a mission-critical activity. To comply with clause 5.9 of ISO/IEC 17025:2005, laboratories must establish quality control procedures. These procedures are needed to monitor and assess the validity of the data obtained from testing and calibration activities and to identify statistical trends. As with the requirements for sampling (see Chapter 22), applied statistical methodologies should be used for data assessment. It is important to remember that the monitoring process must be planned. Elements such as retesting or the recalibration of retained items must be considered as part of the overall monitoring process. A final point pertains to the steps required when analyzed data fall outside of the predefined parameters. This chapter discusses proactive steps that can be taken to achieve compliance with clause 5.9 of ISO/IEC 17025:2005.

Summary of ISO/IEC 17025:2005 Requirement 5.9 (Assuring the Quality of Test and Calibration Results)

- Laboratories must establish written procedures to monitor the validity of testing and calibration activities. Test and calibration data must be recorded in a manner that facilitates data analysis and identification of statistical trends. The application of acceptable statistical methodologies is always considered a best practice when performing data analysis. The monitoring of laboratory data should always be planned and approved in advance. Elements to be considered as part of the overall approach to data monitoring are:

  —The use of certified reference materials

  —The use of certified reference standards

  —Participation in interlaboratory comparison programs

  —A proficiency test (PT) program

  —A test and calibration replication program (repeatability testing)

  —Verification of testing and calibration against laboratory retains (retained samples)

  —Correlation of results employing different operational/ functional characteristics

  Note: The selected approach must always be relevant to the type of testing or calibration being performed.

- Data should always be adequately analyzed for compliance with customer requirements or specifications or established standards. When data are found to be outside of the defined requirements or operating parameters, corrective action must be pursued to ensure only correct and accurate results are being reported.

EFFECTIVE TOOLS FOR IMPLEMENTATION AND COMPLIANCE

Laboratories must establish quality control procedures to ensure the data obtained during the execution of testing and calibration are valid. When developing new procedures for testing and calibration, laboratories must carefully consider all requirements necessary for effective quality control. These requirements should be documented as part of the quality control procedures. Where necessary, existing quality control procedures should be assessed for their adequacy. The laboratory's quality control procedures must contain sufficient granularity to prevent erroneous testing and calibration results from being reported to the customer. When establishing a procedure, the following suggestions for monitoring the validity of results and detecting trends should be considered.

Regular Use of Certified Reference Materials

The definition for certified reference materials (CRMs) is "reference material characterized by a metrologically valid procedure for one or more specified properties, accompanied by a certificate that provides the value of the specified property, its associated uncertainty, and a statement of metrological traceability" (*ISO Guide 30:1992/Amendment 1:2008*). According to the Institute for Reference Materials and Measurements (IRMM):

> Public confidence in measurement results is important in many aspects of modern society, including consumer protection in food consumption, health-care, environmental protection, and fair trade. Certified Reference Materials (CRMs) are cornerstones of modern analytical quality assurance because they allow calibration of instruments, validation of methods, and quality control of methods and laboratories based on traceability and comparability of measurement results. (European Commission Joint Research Centre—IRMM 2012)

Many CRMs are available commercially to support testing and calibration activities. When a laboratory procures a CRM from a supplier, best practice is to get procurement specifications for each CRM purchased. Some CRMs require controlled environmental conditions for storage to ensure their validity is sustained. Special requirements for handling and storage should be documented within each CRM's procurement specification (as applicable). When procured, CRMs should always be accompanied by a certificate. The certificate should state the property and values certified and the procedure by which traceability to SI units or a national standard has been established. Each value certified on the certificate should be supported by a statement of measurement uncertainty at a stated level of confidence.

Another source for CRMs is NIST, which maintains about a thousand high-quality reference materials that laboratories can use for testing and calibration (see Figure 24.1). Many commercial entities such as Sigma-Aldrich are also capable of providing high-quality standards. The Sigma-Aldrich website (http://www.sigmaaldrich.com) provides additional information pertaining to CRMs and links that can give laboratories relevant regulatory and statutory information.

Internal Quality Control Using Secondary Reference Materials

Companies such as Sigma-Aldrich provide detailed traceability and assay results with their standard reference materials (Figure 24.2). Laboratories must ensure that traceability requirements for such secondary reference materials are defined in the quality control procedure. Copies of all certifications for secondary reference standards must be retained, and the laboratory procedures must specify the requirement for certification retention, including retention periods.

National Institute of Standards & Technology

Certificate

Standard Reference Material 1002d

Surface Flammability Standard

This Standard Reference Material (SRM) is intended for use in checking the operation of radiant-panel test equipment in accordance with the calibration and standardization techniques described in ASTM Standard E162-78, Test for Surface Flammability of Materials Using a Radiant Heat Source.

This SRM consists of four sheets of tempered fibrous-felted hardboard, 457 x 152 x 6 mm (18 x 6 x 1/4 in). It is certified for its Flame Spread Index, I, and its Heat Evolution Factor, Q.

Property	Number of Tests	Value	Coefficient of Variation (%)
Flame Spread Index, I	15	203	5.2
Heat Evolution Factor, Q	15	42.0	3.8

The coefficient of variation is the ratio of the standard deviation to the average value expressed as a percent.

Tests over a month period were made on the smoother side (opposite the label) of representative samples of this lot, which had previously been dried and conditioned (see Conditioning).

The wire mesh screen previously required when testing this SRM was not used for recertification testing. More even burning and well defined flame fronts are obtained without the wire screen.

Conditioning: Before testing, SRM 1002d must be dried for 24 hours at 60 °C, and then conditioned to equilibrium at 23 ± 3 °C and 50 ± 5 percent relative humidity.

This SRM is anticipated to have an indefinite shelf-life under normal use and storage conditions.

The tests and measurements leading to the certification of this SRM were performed by J.R. Lawson of the NIST Center for Fire Research.

The technical and support aspects involved in the preparation, certification, and issuance of this Standard Reference Material were coordinated through the Office of Standard Reference Materials by R.W. Seward and A. Dragoo.

August 24, 1989
Gaithersburg, MD 20899

Stanley D. Rasberry, Chief
Office of Standard Reference Materials

Figure 24.1 Example of a NIST CRM certificate.

PT Programs and Participation in Interlaboratory Comparison Programs

According to NIST:

A proficiency test (PT) is simply a method that you may use to validate a particular measurement process. The artifact's reference value is not known by the participating laboratory at the time of its measurement (test). In a well-designed proficiency test, the reference value for the artifact should be principally determined by a competent

Traceability Assay Results

Specification: 97.0–103.0% (anhydrous, USP/NF) (1)
98.5–101.0% (dried substance, EP)

Determination Method: HPLC (ref., USP32: Ibuprofen) (2)

columns:	ProteCol-GP C18 125, 4.6 x 250 mm
mobile phase:	Acetontirile/Water/chloroacetic acid (600:600:4)
column temp.:	30 °C
flow rate:	2 mL/min (3)
injection:	5 μL
detector wavelength:	254 nm

Assay vs. USP Reference Standard (as is basis)

Assay Value (5)
99.5%

vs. USP LOT (4)
K0J008
Labeled Content = 0.999 mg/mg

(1) Product specification

(2) Reference to pharmacopeia monograph (if available) used for the certification

(3) Analytical conditions of the used method

(4) Reference to pharmacopeia lot of the primary standard

(5) Assay value (traceable to the given pharmacopeia lot)

Figure 24.2 Example of a Sigma-Aldrich traceability certification.

laboratory with appropriate traceability to the International System of Units (SI). The reference laboratory should also have demonstrated its competency through key comparisons, inter-laboratory comparisons, or proficiency tests appropriate to validate their measurement capability. It is also preferable that the laboratory has had its competency independently assessed through the process of laboratory accreditation. Lastly, in order to appropriately validate the measurement capability of the participating laboratory, the uncertainty assigned to the artifact by the reference laboratory should be sufficiently smaller than the expanded uncertainty reported by the participating laboratory. (Gust 2012, 1)

A laboratory should participate in at least two PT programs annually for each laboratory discipline. The PT program must cover all functional areas for which the laboratory has received accreditation. Failure to perform PT can result in the laboratory's loss of accreditation.

NIST recommends that laboratories develop and employ a proficiency testing plan (PTP) to substantiate the quality, accuracy, and repeatability of test and calibration results. Employing PTPs is an excellent way for laboratories to comply with the requirement to monitor the validity of test and calibration results and the overall validation of a laboratory's measurement process.

According to the National Association for Proficiency Testing:

Several different methodologies are used to evaluate and report the results of a proficiency test. ISO Guide 43, Proficiency Testing by Inter-laboratory Comparisons—Annex A, provides guidance. NCSLI Recommended Practice, Guide for Inter-laboratory Comparisons, is another excellent source of information. The most widely accepted method compares the measured data against established reference values. The result is the En (called E sub n) number. When the En is between +1 and −1 no corrective action is required. A second method for evaluating and reporting proficiency test results centers around determining the inclusion and/or overlap of a participant's measured values and associated uncertainties with that of the artifact's reported reference values and uncertainties. This evaluation is simply given as "Within," "In," and "Out." Both of these evaluations can be displayed using charts/graphs, making a relatively simple comparison. Besides being compared in the reference values, a report is also prepared showing the data from all participants. With this information it is relatively easy to note individual performance compared to that of peers within the industry. (National Association for Proficiency Testing n.d.)

Test and Calibration Replication Employing Different Methods

According to the FDA's Office of Regulatory Affairs (ORA):

> Replicate testing may be performed on samples which are found to be violative. The original sample results are verified by using an alternative method or by rechecking results by the same method. A violative chemistry result may be verified by a second instrument, another method, a second analyst or repeated by the same analyst. A violative microbiology result by a rapid screening method is verified by a culture method. (FDA Office of Regulatory Affairs 2012)

Retesting and Recalibration of Retained Items

The retesting of retained items is nothing more than the reintroduction of retained items into the normal testing or calibration environment to assess the ongoing performance of the laboratory. The expectation is to establish a history of repeatable testing and calibration results.

Correlation of Results for Different Item Characteristics

According to ORA:

> Checking for correlation means evaluating the interrelated characteristics (analytes) of the sample. By comparing results from different analyses on the same test item, one checks for reasonableness (i.e., Does the data make sense or correspond as anticipated?). Certain characteristics within the sample will maintain an analogous relationship to one another with regard to the type of test

being performed. If one characteristic is dependent on or at all indicative of another characteristic, they should be compared for consistency. The supervisor or designated reviewer should be able to anticipate and recognize an analogous relationship with different characteristics of the same sample. Any deviation, such as the absence of expected primary characteristics or the sudden appearance of previously unobserved characteristics of the sample, signals the probability of error. (FDA Office of Regulatory Affairs 2012)

Analysis of Quality Control Data

One way to analyze quality control data is to use applied statistical methodologies. Best laboratory practice is to ensure all data sheets containing test results or calibration results are assessed for accuracy and acceptability. The laboratory should establish control limits and document them in a procedure. If during the execution of testing or calibration the measured data are found to fall within the control limits, then the data should be deemed acceptable.

Other tools such as accuracy and control charts can be used to determine if the laboratory's measurement system process can provide accurate and repeatable results. Control charts are great tools for quickly identifying data patterns that help in identifying process variation and assignable causes.

Data Found to Be Outside Predefined Criteria

When data are found to be outside the predefined criteria or control limits, then corrective action is required to mitigate the out-of-tolerance condition. The first step should be analyzing the data for transcription errors, calculation errors, equipment setup errors, and sample preparation errors. Using a new set of standards or recalibrating the instrument employed for the initial measurements may be necessary.

QUESTIONS TO CONSIDER DURING AN AUDIT

The questions in this section are not intended to be an all-inclusive list to be built into an internal or external audit checklist. However, they are relevant when evaluating the laboratory's test and calibration results.

1. Does the laboratory have an established procedure for monitoring the validity of testing and calibrations performed?

2. Are results of testing and calibration recorded in a manner such that trends in data can be assessed?

3. Does the laboratory apply statistical techniques in support of data review and analysis?

4. How does the laboratory handle data when the data reflect that the results obtained were outside of the defined limits?

5. Is corrective action pursued when incorrect results have been reported to a customer?

CHAPTER REVIEW

Laboratories must ensure that the results of testing and calibration are accurate and repeatable. There are a number of different tools that can be used by laboratories to ensure they achieve consistency. ISO/IEC 17025 suggests five processes that have proven to be effective for assuring the quality of test and calibration results:

1. Regular use of certified reference materials and/or internal quality control using secondary reference materials

2. Participation in interlaboratory comparison or PT programs

3. Replication of tests or calibrations using the same or different methods

4. Retesting or recalibration of retained items

5. Correlation of results for different characteristics of an item

Using control charts and statistical techniques for data analysis and having a dedicated laboratory resource to provide a thorough review of test and calibration results will ensure customers receive acceptable results, quantified by acceptable data, on a continuous basis.

25

Reporting the Results

Accurately reporting results is as important as protecting the integrity of testing and calibration measurements and data. Clause 5.10 of ISO/IEC 17025:2005 indicates that the results of testing and calibration activities must be: (1) accurate, (2) clear, (3) unambiguous, (4) objective, and (5) in accordance with methods employed for calibration. Depending on the structure of the contract, results may not actually be reported but are retained by laboratories and made available upon customer demand. Calibration certificates created and issued by laboratories have specific reporting requirements. Some of the basic information that may be required include title, laboratory name and address, and customer name and address. Similar mandatory inputs are required for test reports. The standard has very specific requirements that will be reviewed as part of this chapter's material. If testing and calibration was performed by a subcontractor, this too must be reported. No set format or style requirements exist for a test report or calibration certificate; however, creating a template for consistency is highly recommended. This chapter will present samples of a test report and a calibration certificate.

Summary of ISO/IEC 17025:2005 Requirement 5.10 (Reporting the Results)

General

- Laboratories must report the results of testing and calibration work accurately.

- The results of testing and calibration should be reported using a readable test report format or a calibration certificate.

- Depending on the customer (internal or external), simplifying the report or reporting using the customer's format may be acceptable. However, all data relating to the testing or calibration must be retained and be made available upon request.

Note: Typical names associated with reports and certifications are test reports, test certificates, calibration reports, and calibration certificates.

Note: Reports and certificates can be issued as hard-copy documents or electronic records.

Test Reports and Calibration Certificates

- Reports and certificates documenting testing and calibration activities should contain:

  —A report title

  —Laboratory name and address

  —The name and address of the location if work was performed elsewhere

  —Test and/or certificate number

  —Customer name and address

  —List of test or calibration method(s) employed

  —Description and condition of items received

  —Date received

—Sampling plans used

—Result of testing and calibration

—Name and signature of person approving the report or certificate

—Statement of results

Note: Reports and certificates should include page numbers.

Note: Reports and certificates should include a disclaimer such as, "Laboratory reports and certificates cannot be reproduced without prior approval from the laboratory."

Test Reports

- Test reports may also require the following information, as applicable:

  —Deviations, exclusions, and pertinent information relevant to the test method employed or the environmental conditions in which a test was performed

  —A statement of conformance or nonconformance with requirements

  —A statement pertaining to measurement uncertainty

  —Interpretations of the test data and results of testing

  —Customer-specific information

- If sampling plans were used, the following information may also need to be included:

  —The date the sampling took place

  —Clear identification of the sample(s)

  —Sample location and supporting documentation

  —Identification of applicable sampling plan used

  —Relevant environmental conditions

  —A list of other relevant standards and procedures used to support sampling

Calibration Certificates

- When deemed appropriate, calibration certificates must contain this additional information:

  —Relevant environmental conditions

  —Measurement uncertainty

  —Statement of conformity with a recognized standard

  —Proof of measurement traceability

- Calibration certificates should be specific to the work performed and reference only applicable requirements, standards, and clauses.

- When the actual measurement results are not reported, the data must be retained and made available upon request.

- Measurement uncertainty must always be considered when stating the results and overall compliance.

- All results, before and after, must be reported when equipment being calibrated is adjusted or repaired.

- Calibration stickers and certificates should contain a calibration interval suggested by the customer.

Opinions and Interpretations

- Opinions and interpretations made by laboratories must be supported by written rationales that include the basis for the opinion and interpretation.

Note: Opinions and interpretations are just that and should not be confused with actual inspection or test results.

Note: Elements to be considered when offering opinions and interpretations in a test report are: (1) opinions pertaining to the results, (2) opinions pertaining to the contract, (3) opinions related to recommendations, and (4) opinions related to improvements.

Note: Communicating opinions and interpretations directly to the customer is acceptable.

Testing and Calibration Results Obtained from Subcontractors

- Test results obtained from subcontractors must be clearly identified as such in test reports.

- Reports issued by subcontractors can be hard copy or electronic.

- Subcontractors must issue calibration certificates when they perform the work.

Electronic Transmission of Results

- Transmitting results electronically is an acceptable practice.

Format of Reports and Certificates

- The format should be suitable for ensuring information delineated within the report and/or certificate is clear, concise, and unambiguous.

Note: Special consideration should be given to the construction and layout of calibration certificates. Once a satisfactory template has been created, the laboratory should keep it.

Note: Headers on the certificates should be standardized.

Amendments to Test Reports and Calibration Certificates

- Amendments to reports shall be clearly documented. For example, terms such as "amended report" or "corrected report" should be part of the title or be included in a statement that clearly reflects that the report is a revision. If a completely new report is issued, this information needs to be reflected, including a statement to the effect that the new report replaces the original.

EFFECTIVE TOOLS FOR IMPLEMENTATION AND COMPLIANCE

When all test and/or calibration work has been completed, laboratories need to quantify the results and report them in a test report or calibration certificate. To ensure customers are able to quickly find and review relevant information in test reports and calibration certificates, laboratories should standardize the format of these documents. If the customer requires specific information to be reported in a test report or calibration certificate, the requirement should be included in the contract.

Test Reports

ISO/IEC 17025:2005 has specific requirements for the information included in a test report. Laboratories must include this information. Once the test report has been printed and issued, the laboratory must ensure that the data used to populate the test report are retained for the time period specified within the laboratory's control of records procedure (see Chapter 13). Figure 25.1 depicts an example of a test report for an accelerometer.

Calibration Certificates

ISO/IEC 17025:2005 has specific requirements for the information included in a calibration certificate. Laboratories must include this information. Once the certificate has been printed and issued, the laboratory must ensure that the data used to populate the calibration certificate are retained for the time period specified within the laboratory's control of records procedure (see Chapter 13). A good example of a calibration certificate can be seen in Figure 25.2.

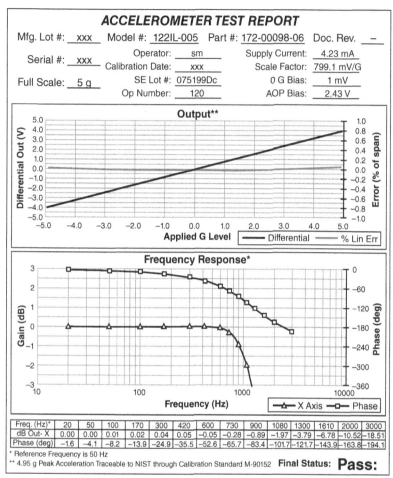

Figure 25.1   Example of a test report.

Amendments to Test Reports and Calibration Certificates

A laboratory may need to revise a test report or calibration certificate or issue a new (replacement) test report or calibration certificate. The process of revision or replacement cannot be performed informally. If a test report or calibration certificate is revised, the word "revised" must makes its way into the report or certificate. If the test report or calibration certificate is replaced, a reference to the original must be included

CERTIFICATE OF CALIBRATION

Product Identification

Product Type:	N/A	Customer Name:	N/A
Model:	N/A	Customer PO:	N/A
Serial No.*:	101083A	Order Code:	LEBOW1
Part No.:	3145-CS-25K	Instrument Serial No.:	N/A

* A letter at the end of the serial number indicates the associated bridge

Product Specifications

Capacity:	N/A	Excitation:	N/A
Calibrated At:	25000.00lbs	Amplifier Output:	N/A
Direction / Type:	Compression	Electrical Leakage:	∞ MegΩ

Calibration Data

Input Resistance:	354 Ω	Calibration Factor:	-3.9961mV/V	Calibration Date:	06/21/2010
Output Resistance:	351 Ω	Operator(s):	KEVIN		

Calibration Procedure: 072-FP75-23, Rev -, Date 02/19/2008

Remarks

N/A

Manufactured/Received Data: NA After Adjustment/Repair Data: NA

Environmental Data

Temperature: 75 °F Humidity: 53 %RH Pressure: 14.30 psiA

Calibration Standards

NIST Traceable #	Inst. ID#	Description	Model	Cal Date	Date Due
3642653	200114	25K LOAD CELL	CS20-25K-B000	11/02/2009	11/02/2011
4058916	201072	DIGITAL MULTIMETER	45	04/13/2010	04/13/2011
3834763	7241526	TRANSDUCER SIMULATOR	TS-10-2	01/25/2010	01/25/2011

Calibration Data

% Capacity	Load (lbs)	Raw (mV/V)	Normalized (mV/V)
0	0.00	-0.0133	0.0000
10	2500.00	-0.4121	-0.3987
20	5000.00	-0.8126	-0.7993
30	7500.00	-1.2116	-1.1983
40	10000.00	-1.6110	-1.5977
50	12500.00	-2.0105	-1.9972
60	15000.00	-2.4105	-2.3971
70	17500.00	-2.8096	-2.7963
80	20000.00	-3.2104	-3.1971
90	22500.00	-3.6092	-3.5959
100	25000.00	-4.0098	-3.9965
90	22500.00	-3.6097	-3.5963
80	20000.00	-3.2112	-3.1979
70	17500.00	-2.8102	-2.7969
60	15000.00	-2.4118	-2.3985
50	12500.00	-2.0124	-1.9991
40	10000.00	-1.6123	-1.5989
30	7500.00	-1.2127	-1.1993
20	5000.00	-0.8134	-0.8000
10	2500.00	-0.4124	-0.3990
0	0.00	-0.0134	0.0000

Manufactured/Received Data After Adjustment/Repair Data

Shunt Resistor 1	300000
Shunt Sense 1	-ShuntCal(Sig)+Sense
Zero 1	-0.01338 mV/V
Shunt Zero 1	0.33%
Shunt Cal. 1	-2.88047 mV/V
Shunt Cal. Capacity 1	18018.74895 lbs

Certificate No

101083A--001

PRINT DATE: 6/29/2010

Document No. 086-1000-03

Figure 25.2 Example of a calibration certificate.

in the replacement report or certificate. Records supporting all amendments must be retained.

QUESTIONS TO CONSIDER DURING AN AUDIT

The questions in this section are not intended to be an all-inclusive list to be built into an internal or external audit

checklist. However, they are relevant when evaluating the over-all effectiveness of a laboratory's reporting of results for testing and calibration.

1. How does the laboratory report the results of testing and calibration work?

2. Do test reports contain information relevant to the testing performed and in accordance with requirements delineated in clause 5.10.3 of ISO/IEC 17025:2005?

3. Do calibration certificates contain information relevant to the calibration performed and in accordance with requirements delineated in clause 5.10.4 of ISO/IEC 17025:2005?

4. Are calibration certificates free of recommendations for calibration intervals?

5. If equipment has been repaired prior to calibration, is this information documented on the calibration certificate?

6. Does the laboratory offer opinions and interpretations of test and calibration results?

7. Are opinions and interpretations made by qualified individuals?

8. When the laboratory employs subcontractors for testing and calibration, are the subcontractors required to provide test reports and calibration certificates?

9. Does the laboratory permit the electronic transfer of test reports and calibration certificates?

10. How does the laboratory handle the amendment of test reports and calibration certificates?

CHAPTER REVIEW

ISO/IEC 17025 requires specific information to be included in test reports and calibration certificates. Laboratories must ensure their reports and certificates comply with these requirements. Once test reports and calibration certificates have been generated, the data used to populate these documents must be retained in accordance with the laboratory's control of records procedure. Amendments to test reports and calibration certificates (revisions and replacements) must be adequately documented with traceability back to the original documents. Terms such as "revised," "amended," and "replacement" must find their way into the new certificates and reports.

Epilogue

I hope you have been able to glean value from this book. Quality and regulatory professionals must understand so many regulations and standards, including changes, that trying to remain current with these requirements is a never-ending task. ISO 9001:2008 and ISO 13485:2003 are quality system standards most readers are probably familiar with, while ISO/IEC 17025:2005 may be less familiar. That said, understanding the basic concepts in ISO/IEC 17025 will only enhance readers' understanding of the calibration requirements delineated in ISO 9001 and ISO 13485. In closing, thank you for taking the time to read *Implementing ISO/IEC 17025:2005: A Practical Guide.*

Best wishes,
Bob Mehta

Bibliography

21 CFR 820 (Quality System Regulation), April 1, 2012.

American Association for Laboratory Accreditation. 2007. *R103—General Requirements: Proficiency Testing for ISO/IEC 17025 Laboratories.* http://www.a2la.org/requirements/. Accessed November 26, 2012.

————. 2010. *Technical Staff Matrix for Accreditation—ISO/IEC 17025.* http://www.a2la.org/forms/technical_staff_matrix.pdf. Accessed July 30, 2012.

ANSI/ASQ Z1.4-2008: Sampling Procedures and Inspection by Attributes. 2008. American National Standards Institute and American Society for Quality.

ANSI/ASQ Z1.9-2008: Sampling Procedures and Tables for Inspection by Variables for Percent Nonconforming. 2008. American National Standards Institute and American Society for Quality.

AssurX. n.d. *CATSWeb.* http://www.assurx.com/product-technology-overview.htm. Accessed August 8, 2012.

ASTM International. n.d. *ASTM Procedure List.* http://www.astm.org/Standard/index.shtml. Accessed August 2, 2012.

Carlson, C. S. n.d. *Key Factors for Effective FMEAs.* ReliaSoft. http://www.reliasoft.com/newsletter/v6i2/fmea_factors.htm. Accessed November 15, 2012.

Doiron, T., and J. Beers. 1991. *The Gauge Block Handbook.* http://xa.yimg.com/kq/groups/2573836/494330063/. Accessed November 18, 2012.

Engineering Change Request. 2012. Clinivation website. http://www. clinivation.com/pages/resources/downloads.php. Accessed October 24, 2012.

European Commission Joint Research Centre—IRMM (Institute for Reference Materials and Measurements). 2012. "Certified Reference Materials 2012–2013." http://irmm.jrc.ec.europa.eu/reference_ materials_catalogue/. Accessed November 26, 2012.

FDA Office of Regulatory Affairs. 2012. *Laboratory Manual of Quality Policies for ORA Regulatory Laboratories.* http://web.ora. fda.gov/dfs/policies/manuals/default.htm. Accessed November 28, 2012.

Gravel, N. 2012. "QC Failures Happen: Methods for Determining Which Undesirable Conditions Require Root Cause Analysis and Which Do Not." *Lab Manager Magazine,* July 6. http://www. labmanager.com/?articles.view/articleNo/8083/article/QC-Failures-Happen/.

Gust, J. C. n.d. *Developing a Proficiency Testing Plan for Your Laboratory.* National Institute of Standards and Technology. http:// www.nist.gov/pml/wmd/labmetrology/upload/dev-prof-test-gust.pdf. Accessed November 18, 2012.

Honeywell International. n.d. "Calibration Certificate Examples." https://measurementsensors.honeywell.com/customer/repair/ calibration_certificate_examples/Pages/default.aspx. Accessed November 29, 2012.

IndySoft. "Gage InSite Commercial Lab Edition." http://www. indysoft.com/gage-insite-commercial-lab-edition.htm. Accessed November 24, 2012.

ISO 14644-1:1999: Cleanrooms and associated controlled environments—Part 1, Classification of air cleanliness. 1999. Geneva, Switzerland: International Organization for Standardization.

ISO 19011:2011: Guidelines for auditing management systems, 2nd ed. 2011. Geneva, Switzerland: International Organization for Standardization.

ISO 9001:2008: Quality management systems—Requirements. 2008. Geneva, Switzerland: International Organization for Standardization.

ISO Guide 30:1992/Amendment 1:2008: Revision of definitions for reference material and certified reference material. 2008. Geneva, Switzerland: International Organization for Standardization.

ISO/IEC 17011:2004: Conformity assessment—General requirements for accreditation bodies accrediting conformity assessment bodies, 2nd ed. 2004. Geneva, Switzerland: International Organization for Standardization.

ISO/IEC 17025:2005: General requirements for the competence of testing and calibration laboratories, 2nd ed. 2005. Geneva, Switzerland: International Organization for Standardization.

ISPE. 2011. *GAMP Good Practice Guide: A Risk-Based Approach to Calibration Management.* Available at http://www.ispe.org/gamp-good-practice-guide/calibration-management-attachments/. Accessed November 24, 2012.

Kelly Donaldson Law. n.d. "Contract Review Checklist." http://www.kellydonaldsonlaw.com/Contract_Review_Checklist.pdf. Accessed October 25, 2012.

Metaltest. n.d. "Metal Test Quality Policy." http://www.metaltest-inc.com/about-metaltest/quality-policy.html. Accessed August 1, 2012.

Mind Tools. n.d. "Managing Complaints and Feedback: Improving the Ways That You Do Things." http://www.mindtools.com/pages/article/managing-complaints.htm. Accessed November 3, 2012.

NASA. 2010. *Measurement Uncertainty Analysis Principles and Methods.* http://www.hq.nasa.gov/office/codeq/doctree/NHBK873919-3.pdf. Accessed November 18, 2012.

National Association for Proficiency Testing. n.d. "The Value of Proficiency Testing." http://www.proficiency.org/NewsUpdates/TheValueOfProficienyTesting/tabid/123/Default.aspx#whypart. Accessed November 26, 2012.

National Association of Testing Authorities (NATA). 2012. *Technical Note 17—Guidelines for the Validation and Verification of Quantitative and Qualitative Test Methods.* http://www.nata.asn.au/phocadownload/publications/Technical_publications/. Accessed November 18, 2012.

National Institute of Standards and Technology (NIST). 2012. *Internal Audit Checklist Form ISO/IEC 17025:2005.* http://www.nist.gov/pml/ wmd/labmetrology/upload/isoiec-17025-chklst-09.docx. Accessed October 27, 2012.

NIST/SEMATECH. 2012. *NIST/SEMATECH E-Handbook of Statistical Methods.* http://www.itl.nist.gov/div898/handbook/index.htm. Accessed November 24, 2012.

Saders, Scott D. 2011. *How to Perform Laboratory Internal Audits.* Illinois Water Environment Association's Train the Trainer Seminar, October 20. http://www.iweasite.org/Laboratory/2011_lab_smr_ audits.pdf. Accessed November 10, 2012.

Silicon Designs. n.d. "Example Test Report for Surface Mount Accelerometers." http://www.silicondesigns.com/examples.html. Accessed November 29, 2012.

Tague, N. 2005. *The Quality Toolbox*, 2nd edition. Milwaukee, WI: ASQ Quality Press.

United Nations Industrial Development Organization. 2006. *Role of Measurement and Calibration in the Manufacture of Products for the Global Market.*

———. 2009. *Complying with ISO 17025: A Practical Guidebook for Meeting the Requirements of Laboratory Accreditation Schemes Based on ISO 17025:2005 or Equivalent National Standard.* http:// www.unido.org/fileadmin/user_media/Publications/Pub_free/ Complying_with_ISO_17025_A_practical_guidebook.pdf.

Westcott, R. 2005. "Corrective vs. Preventive Action." *Quality Progress Magazine,* March, 104–105.

Index

Note: Page numbers followed by *f* refer to figures; those followed by *t* refer to tables.

A

accommodation. *See* environmental conditions; facilities management
American Association for Laboratory Accreditation (A2LA), 35
ANSI/ASQ Z1.4-2008, 158, 160
ANSI/ASQ Z1.9-2008, 160
AS9100, 3, 9, 85
audit checklist, 96*f*

C

CATSWeb, 46, 74
certified reference materials (CRMs), 159, 173–174, 175*f*
cleanrooms and controlled environments, 124–125
closed-loop feedback process, 57–58, 57*f*
complaint forms, 59*f*. *See also* customer complaints
computer software. *See also specific software*
    corrective action, 74–75
    document control, 18, 20, 46
    purchasing, 46
    test data control, 137
confidentiality, 6, 85, 137

continuous improvement, 68–72
    corrective action/preventive action (CAPA), 70
    customer feedback, 68, 70
    data analysis, 70
    ISO/IEC 17025:2005 (requirement 4.10), 68–69
    management review, 71
    quality assurance audits, 70
    quality assurance objectives, 69–70
    quality assurance policy, 69
contracts. *See* requests, tenders, and contracts
control of records. *See* document control; record control
corrective action, 73–79
    customer feedback, 73
    investigative tools, 75
    ISO 9001:2008, 73
    ISO/IEC 17025:2005 (requirement 4.11), 74
    quality management systems (QMS), 73
    verification of effectiveness (VOE), 75, 98
corrective action/preventive action (CAPA)
    facilities management, 8
    follow-up, 78

The Knowledge Center
www.asq.org/knowledge-center

Learn about quality. Apply it. Share it.

ASQ's online Knowledge Center is the place to:

- Stay on top of the latest in quality with Editor's Picks and Hot Topics.

- Search ASQ's collection of articles, books, tools, training, and more.

- Connect with ASQ staff for personalized help hunting down the knowledge you need, the networking opportunities that will keep your career and organization moving forward, and the publishing opportunities that are the best fit for you.

Use the Knowledge Center Search to quickly sort through hundreds of books, articles, and other software-related publications.

www.asq.org/knowledge-center

The Global Voice of Quality™

Ask a Librarian

<u>Did you know?</u>

- The ASQ Quality Information Center contains a wealth of knowledge and information available to ASQ members and non-members

- A librarian is available to answer research requests using ASQ's ever-expanding library of relevant, credible quality resources, including journals, conference proceedings, case studies and Quality Press publications

- ASQ members receive free internal information searches and reduced rates for article purchases

- You can also contact the Quality Information Center to request permission to reuse or reprint ASQ copyrighted material, including journal articles and book excerpts

- For more information or to submit a question, visit **http://asq.org/knowledge-center/ask-a-librarian-index**

Visit **www.asq.org/qic for more information.**

TRAINING CERTIFICATION CONFERENCES MEMBERSHIP **PUBLICATIONS**

The Global Voice of Quality™

Belong to the Quality Community!

Established in 1946, ASQ is a global community of quality experts in all fields and industries. ASQ is dedicated to the promotion and advancement of quality tools, principles, and practices in the workplace and in the community.

The Society also serves as an advocate for quality. Its members have informed and advised the U.S. Congress, government agencies, state legislatures, and other groups and individuals worldwide on quality-related topics.

Vision

By making quality a global priority, an organizational imperative, and a personal ethic, ASQ becomes the community of choice for everyone who seeks quality technology, concepts, or tools to improve themselves and their world.

ASQ is...

- More than 90,000 individuals and 700 companies in more than 100 countries

- The world's largest organization dedicated to promoting quality

- A community of professionals striving to bring quality to their work and their lives

- The administrator of the Malcolm Baldrige National Quality Award

- A supporter of quality in all sectors including manufacturing, service, healthcare, government, and education

- YOU

Visit www.asq.org for more information.

TRAINING CERTIFICATION CONFERENCES MEMBERSHIP **PUBLICATIONS**

ASQ Membership

Research shows that people who join associations experience increased job satisfaction, earn more, and are generally happier*. ASQ membership can help you achieve this while providing the tools you need to be successful in your industry and to distinguish yourself from your competition. So why wouldn't you want to be a part of ASQ?

Networking

Have the opportunity to meet, communicate, and collaborate with your peers within the quality community through conferences and local ASQ section meetings, ASQ forums or divisions, ASQ Communities of Quality discussion boards, and more.

Professional Development

Access a wide variety of professional development tools such as books, training, and certifications at a discounted price. Also, ASQ certifications and the ASQ Career Center help enhance your quality knowledge and take your career to the next level.

Solutions

Find answers to all your quality problems, big and small, with ASQ's Knowledge Center, mentoring program, various e-newsletters, *Quality Progress* magazine, and industry-specific products.

Access to Information

Learn classic and current quality principles and theories in ASQ's Quality Information Center (QIC), *ASQ Weekly* e-newsletter, and product offerings.

Advocacy Programs

ASQ helps create a better community, government, and world through initiatives that include social responsibility, Washington advocacy, and Community Good Works.

Visit www.asq.org/membership for more information on ASQ membership.

*2008, The William E. Smith Institute for Association Research

TRAINING CERTIFICATION CONFERENCES **MEMBERSHIP PUBLICATIONS**   The Global Voice of Qual